WITHDRAWN

Sully's "GEORGE TICKNOR"
(Reproduced from the Oil Original
in Baker Library at Dartmouth)

George Ticknor's
The Sorrows of Young Werter

THE UNIVERSITY OF NORTH CAROLINA
STUDIES IN COMPARATIVE LITERATURE

Editorial Committee

1. Fernand Baldensperger and Werner P. Friederich: Bibliography of Comparative Literature. 1950. Pp. XXIV and 701.

2. Werner P. Friederich: Dante's Fame Abroad, 1350-1850. The Influence of Dante Alighieri on the Poets and Scholars of Spain, France, England, Germany, Switzerland and the United States. 1950. Pp. 582.

3. R. C. Simonini, Jr.: Italian Scholarship in Renaissance England. 1952. Pp. 125.

Address orders to Richard Jente,
Box 537, Chapel Hill, N. C.

European Sales through Librairie E. Droz
8 Rue Verdaine, Geneva, Switzerland

THE UNIVERSITY OF NORTH CAROLINA
STUDIES IN COMPARATIVE LITERATURE

George Ticknor's
The Sorrows of Young Werter

Goethe, Johann Wolfgang von

Edited with Introduction and Critical Analysis

by

FRANK G. RYDER

Dartmouth College

CHAPEL HILL

NUMBER FOUR   1952

Copyright 1952

The University of North Carolina

Printed in U.S.A. by
The Orange Printshop
Chapel Hill, North Carolina

TABLE OF CONTENTS

Page

Foreword vii

Introduction

  1. George Ticknor ix

  2. Ticknor and the German Language xi

  3. Ticknor and German Literature xvi

  4. Ticknor, Goethe, and *Werther* xviii

  5. The Source of Ticknor's Original xxii

  6. Ticknor and *Werther* in Later Years xxiii

  7. Scholarly Interest in *Werther* xxix

  8. The Text of Ticknor's Translation xxxii

THE SORROWS OF YOUNG WERTER 1

Appendix: The Quality of Ticknor's Translation 96

Notes 105

FOREWORD

Goethe's *Die Leiden des jungen Werthers* owns, in extent of popular influence and critical attention, few peers among European novels. Early American interest in the work was active, partisan, and surprisingly widespread. Yet American acquaintance with *Werther* came entirely through translations of admittedly inferior accuracy and literary quality: primarily the Malthus re-translation from the French, with scattered copies of the lesser-known versions of Pratt and Render. Malthus and Pratt were Englishmen by birth, Render, by adoption. Until the Goethe Bicentennial year of 1949 no American apparently had turned his hand to a translation of this remarkable work. No American, that is, save one.

In two puzzling passages from famous works of the preceding century there is trace of an American translation. Edward Everett, in his pioneering essay on *Dichtung und Wahrheit* in the 1817 *North American Review,* said:

> We cannot dismiss the subject of Werther, without speaking of the form in which it is known to the English reader. We think there are two English translations. The one which we have seen, besides the omission of whole letters and parts of letters, is a miserable catch-penny circulating library production, apparently made from the French. . . . Whether a better one is to be expected from England, whose productions, good and bad, are reprinted in America with such exemplary diligence, we cannot say. Some of our readers have been gratified with the sight of a manuscript translation made at home, which is worthy of the inimitable original.[1]

In introducing his *Life, Letters, and Journals,* George Ticknor, America's great scholar, educator, and chronicler, reviewed in some detail his early acquaintance with the German language. He concluded, "I. . .obtained a copy of Goethe's 'Werther' in German. . . I got so far as to write a translation of 'Werther', but no farther."[2]

These two curious references have the strongest affinity. Everett and Ticknor had met long before their journey to Europe. Everett knew of his friend's determination to learn German and abetted it by securing the loan of a grammar. The two studied in Göttingen together and visited Goethe together. The assumption that Everett's praise was meant for Ticknor's translation is not unavoidable, but certainly likely. Several years before the discovery of the Ticknor manuscript, Orie W. Long, the leading writer on *Werther* in America, quoted Everett's statement as "perhaps a reference to Ticknor's unpublished translation."[3]

Ticknor's translation was never released; it disappeared entirely. In view of the two references to the work, curiosity as to its whereabouts was inevitable. That the manuscript survived at least most of Ticknor's lifetime was obvious from a note, dated 1870, in his manuscript journals: "I have still the original copy of my translation."[4] Search for the manuscript, stimulated particularly by the growing interest in George Ticknor, was extensive but fruitless. The work was given up as lost.

In 1948 I found the manuscript, as yet uncatalogued, in the Alumni Archives of Dartmouth's Baker Library.[5] Search there was natural. It was generally known that Baker Library possessed the manuscript of Ticknor's European journals "and other Ticknor manuscript materials." That *Werther* would be among them was a hope fostered by innocence. Had I been aware of the full extent of previous efforts to locate the manuscript I should have expected nothing.

The manuscript consists of a neat, three-quarter leather notebook with 222 of its pages written in ink in Ticknor's legible hand. It has a title page reading: "The Sorrows of Young Werter—Nov. 23-Dec. 10, 1814." The back of the binding bears no inscription. This is surprising, since most of Ticknor's other manuscripts, similarly bound, are titled (for example, "Belles-Lettres," "German Translation," "Varia"). The book is part of a large bequest which came to Dartmouth in 1943, the gift of the late William Dexter of Boston, a direct descendant of George Ticknor.

Of the work itself this much may be said at the beginning: It is a worthy translation. It shows a degree of accuracy exceptional for its time but not comparable to that of the latest translators, from Boylan to the present. Yet it exhibits a felicity of English, a dignity and sweep of language not excelled in any translation, whatever the date.

FRANK G. RYDER

Hanover, N. H., 1952

INTRODUCTION

1. *George Ticknor*

George Ticknor was America's first great scholar in belles-lettres. As interest in the history of American writing turns to the leaders of literary scholarship his name is inevitably among the most conspicuous. Possessed of a charming personality and indefatigable energy, he transcended the field of scholarship to be a prime mover in educational reform and one of our most fascinating chroniclers. His *History of Spanish Literature* is one of the first major works of American literary scholarship to win unquestioned superiority in the European world of learning. The correspondence and diaries of his *Life, Letters, and Journals* constitute perhaps the most distinguished and absorbing account by an American of studies, travels, and friendships in the Old World. He was a true "literary pioneer."

The story of Ticknor's life is, or should be, well known. There are brief and excellent sketches of his work by Orie W. Long, J.D.M. Ford, Van Wyck Brooks, and Henry Grattan Doyle.[6] His own *Life, Letters, and Journals* is the source *sine qua non*. For this presentation of his *Werther*, only the briefest word is necessary.

George Ticknor was born in 1791. He was educated by his father. Personally examined by President Wheelock of Dartmouth, he was certified for admission to that college when he was not yet ten. At fourteen he entered with advanced standing and graduated in 1807. After a brief turn at the law, which he found incompatible, he resumed his classical studies and subsequently took up the learning of German. He went to Europe in 1815 to study at the University of Göttingen. He and his companion Edward Everett were the first Americans to do serious advanced study on the Continent. Before, during, and after his months at Göttingen he traveled through Europe, through England, Holland, France, Spain, Portugal, and Italy, observing, meeting people, and writing. On his return from Europe he began teaching under the Smith Professorship of the French and Spanish Languages and Literatures at Harvard, and as Professor of Belles-Lettres. His first successors in the Smith chair were Henry Wadsworth Longfellow and James

Russell Lowell. He was a fluent and compelling teacher of
literature and the organizer of the first effective instruction
in modern foreign languages in the United States. Along with
his work as a teacher he led an unceasing battle to modernize
the Harvard curriculum. He fought for the creation of de-
partments, greater freedom of electives, advancement according to ability, for voluntary study and reading, for recitation
as an aspect of instruction, not as a quizzing session. To a
great extent frustrated in these aims he resigned his position
and in 1836 went again to Europe. After his return he was
still active in public and scholarly affairs. His *Spanish Literature* appeared in 1849, was recognized as the prime authority,
and was translated into the major languages of Europe. He
was one of the founders of the Boston Public Library, in whose
interest he returned to Europe in 1856. His *Life of William*
Hickling Prescott occupied a good part of his advanced age. It
appeared in 1864. Though for years he continued active in studies, civic affairs, and wide correspondence, he began in the
last five years of his life a gradual retirement to the calm of
his friends and gardens. He died in 1871.

In many fields—literary scholarship, education, biography,
letters—Ticknor is a deservedly famous man. In none is he so
accessible as in the role of chronicler. For anyone unfamiliar
with his work, the journals and letters are the best avenue of
approach. Their importance does not end there. They are an
American source book of enduring significance. Their scope
and the scope of Ticknor's world can be measured by this list
of his eminent friends, which is drawn without addition or
deletion from Doyle's conservative study: Jefferson, Webster,
Clay, Everett, Irving, Prescott, Motley; Scott, Byron, Southey,
Wordsworth, Macaulay, Ruskin, Hallam, Milman, Lord Holland,
Miss Edgeworth, Melbourne, Palmerston, Russell, Peel, Sir
Humphrey Davy, Sir William Hamilton, Sir Charles Lyell;
Chateaubriand, Lamartine, de Tocqueville, Mme. de Staël, Con-
stant, Sainte-Beuve, Mérimée, Guizot, Lafayette, Talleyrand,
Louis Philippe and the Bonapartes; King John of Saxony,
Schlegel, Wolf, Tieck, Humboldt, Metternich; Moratín, Rivas,
Rivadeneyra, Gayangos; Manzoni, Cavour.[7]

2. *Ticknor and the German Language*

Writing, many years after its completion, of his translation of Wieland's masterpiece, John Quincy Adams said with impressive modesty, "Among my exercises in learning the German language, was a complete translation into English verse of his 'Oberon.' "[8] The magnitude of Adams' concept of "learning the German language" is strikingly paralleled in Ticknor's 1870 footnote to a passage in his first European journal: "Before I left home I translated the whole of Charlotte and Werther—my first real exercise in German."[9]

With Ticknor, as with Adams, a great labor of translation appears under the common guise of learning a foreign language. Ticknor's task was, if anything, more arduous than Adams'. He set himself as high a goal, for the exigencies of Wieland's verse are scarcely more intense than the constant demands of Goethe's impassioned prose. What is more, Ticknor wrote his *Werter* in Boston; his instruction in German was precarious; books and reference works were hard to come by. Adams did his translation while he was Minister at the Prussian Court. His diaries, from March, 1798 when he began to study German to May, 1800, when he finished his *Oberon*, speak of constant reading, study, and formal instruction. The time Ticknor devoted to his study of German is significantly less than Adams' long apprenticeship. He cannot have begun the language very much before the summer of 1814, yet the first date in his manuscript of *Werter* is Nov. 23 of the same year.

In the *Life, Letters, and Journals* Ticknor describes the background and course of his study:

> In consultation with him [his father, to whom he had revealed the demise of his interest in law], it was settled, that . . . I should go to Europe, and study for two or three years. I therefore gave up my office, and turned all my attention and effort to learning what I could of the German language, and German universities, to which my thoughts and wishes had been already turned as the best places for education.
>
> The first intimation I ever had on the subject was from Mme. de Staël's work on Germany, then just published. My next came from a pamphlet, published by Villers,—to defend the University of Göttingen from the ill intentions of Jérome Bonaparate, the King of Westphalia,—in which he gave a sketch of the University, and its courses of study. My astonishment at these revelations was in-

creased by an account of its library, given, by an Englishman who
had been at Göttingen, to my friend, the Rev. Samuel C. Thacher.
I was sure that I should like to study at such a university, but it
was in vain that I endeavored to get farther knowledge upon the
subject. I would gladly have prepared for it by learning the language I should have to use there, but there was no one in Boston who
could teach me.

At Jamaica Plains there was a Dr. Brosius, a native of Stras-
burg, who gave instruction in mathematics. He was willing to do
what he could for me in German, but he warned me that his pro-
nunciation was very bad, as was that of all Alsace, which had become a part of France. Nor was it possible to get books. I borrowed
a Meidinger's Grammar, French and German, from my friend,
Mr. Everett, and sent to New Hampshire, where I knew there was
a German Dictionary, and procured it. I also obtained a copy of
Goethe's "Werther" in German (through Mr. William S. Shaw's
connivance) from amongst Mr. J. Q. Adams's books, deposited by
him, on going to Europe, in the Athenaeum, under Mr. Shaw's
care, but without giving him permission to lend them. I got so far
as to write a translation of "Werther," but no farther.

I was thus occupied through the summer and autumn of 1814. It
was all very agreeable.[10]

The dominant impression of this passage, besides its testimony to Ticknor's youthful determination and energy, is the
prevailing lack of familiarity with German language and letters and the virtual absence of opportunities to acquire any
familiarity. On another occasion, in his *Life of Prescott*, Ticknor emphasizes the lack of facilities for learning German: "A
German instructor, or means for learning the German language,
were not to be had either in Boston or Cambridge."[11] The rest
of the passage cited does not imply better conditions elsewhere.

Ticknor's view was accepted without question by most
scholars. However, our knowledge of the early cultural con-
nections between Germany and New England has been of late
greatly widened, and the newly published evidence[12] has tended,
by revealing the unexpectedly large scope of previous contacts,
to discount first the accuracy and secondly the pioneering contribution of George Ticknor. Ticknor has indeed been accused
of starting by a "slip of memory" (in the above passage) the
"misleading traditional account" that "significant New England-German relations began suddenly about 1814."

The sentence cited from Ticknor's *Life of Prescott* as well as
a similar passage (quoted below) from one of his letters to

Jefferson, dated 1815, prove at least that Ticknor's own memory was not faulty, [13] whatever the facts may have been. And while it is true that we must now recognize a more active occupation with German letters in early New England, it is also true that the new evidence on Ticknor's German studies, of which his *Werter* is a major part, greatly increases both his own stature and the true meaning of "significant New England-German relations." Previous accomplishments, indeed, pale in comparison.

Nor is Ticknor's view of the facts entirely erroneous. Much of the evidence adduced for early familiarity with German letters concerns theological and other scholarly contacts whose medium was Latin or English. The Anthology Society, for example, is often spoken of as furnishing instances of acquaintance, on a high level, with German language and letters.[14] Yet it dealt, as far as the record goes, with only four major works of German origin: Zollikoffer's and Griesbach's theological works,[15] and a quaint item on unguiology[16] (none of them in the German language) and a single subject of literary import, Ticknor's own review of Sotheby's translation of Wieland's *Oberon*, which shows no trace of interest in the language of the original.

Most of the prominent contemporary figures who learned German failed somehow to communicate their interests to larger circles. This is true of William Jenks, whose work on the *Messias* was lost, of Adams, who did nothing further with his *Oberon*, of Buckminster, who studied the language only for theological readings and apparently never mentioned the fact to his friend Ticknor.[17] It is to a large extent the case with the Vaughans, whom Ticknor also knew.[18] (Ticknor, it is true, did not publish his *Werter*, but his German studies lived on among his friends and students in Boston and at Harvard.)

It is mainly on William Bentley that the case for effective knowledge of German must rest, and here the foundations are secure.[19] Bentley started his work in German about 1782 "with a heterogeneous collection of about a dozen German books which he had picked up around Boston and Salem."[20] He even took a few lessons in German. Largely on his own, he acquired a real knowledge of the language. He was active in talking and writing about German literature and got several others started on studies or interests in German. The library of German books which he gradually built up was remarkable. Bentley's articles in the *Impartial Register* were perhaps the most effective agency in acquainting New England with Germany, and they were contemporary with Ticknor's early interests in German. However, until their conversations in 1819, Ticknor's connection with Bentley was apparently limited to a written request for letters of introduction.[21]

Ticknor's distinguished young contemporaries, whose interest in German letters was the admitted starting point of the golden age of German studies in America, present, in knowledge of the language, a far less impressive picture than Bentley. Cogswell and Calvert knew little or no German until their travels. Bancroft, on his arrival at Göttingen, says that he repaired directly to Benecke (Professor of English literature and Second Librarian), "the Patron in chief of all students who speak English only," and began German lessons. [22] Everett, who in 1814, at the age of 19, was Buckminister's successor at Brattle Street Church, may have inherited some interest in German from his predecessor, but his main stimulus was Moses Stuart of Andover, who urged him to translate Herder[23] and who on June 24, 1813, wrote to him, "It affords me much pleasure to find that you have made progress in the German language."[24] Bentley also helped him to review German Homeric studies. Still when Everett was studying at Göttingen, he found his imperfect knowledge of German a handicap.[25] Longfellow had to be assured by Ticknor that he could pick up enough German by the time the session commenced at Göttingen to understand the lectures. Ticknor's own influence was decisive in directing Longfellow's initial efforts among the modern languages to German, rather than to French, Spanish, or Italian. Ticknor's most advanced rival was Everett. Yet the difference between the amount of work the two men did is measured by the comparison of Ticknor's *Werter* with Everett's similarly ambitious project of a translation of Klopstock's *Messias*, which he conceived in 1816 (at Göttingen) and which, in spite of his brother's agreement to do the even-numbered books, he abandoned within the year.

Ticknor's specific word that there was no one in Boston to teach him German merits examination. There are instances of earlier opportunities for German study.[26] Frederick Jordy, Bentley's brief tutor, ran an advertisement in the *Imperial Register* in 1800, offering German lessons. Copies of Ludwig's dictionary appeared in early Eighteenth Century New England libraries; the Bailey-Arnold dictionary and Bachmeier's grammar appeared in America about mid-century. Bentley, as early as 1797, lent Jenks Gottsched's German grammar. Yet these and similar facts amount to a chance teacher here, a grammar or dictionary there. They do not affect the substantial validity and importance of Ticknor's statement that there was no one in Boston to teach him, not do they essentially contradict the impression gained from the passage in the *Life, Letters, and Journals* that it was difficult to get books for German study. The general rule is more important than the exception, at least for the broad cultural picture. Stephen Longfellow, for example, writes in a language-conscious letter to his son in 1827, "There is no gentleman in this state [Maine] who is master of the German language,"[27]—*pace* Benjamin Vaughan at Hallowell.[28]

In the field of formal instruction on an advanced level, the pioneering role of Ticknor, and the general vacuum that preceded, is apparent in many ways. Ticknor was instrumental, for example, in getting Blaettermann his position at the University of Virginia in 1825. This was the first major appointment, even part time, of a professor of German in the United States. When Follen, another "Ticknor man," prepared his reader for use at Harvard, he turned to Ticknor's library as a source for his selections. Follen was the first official instructor in German at Harvard, though as early as 1816 the Corporation had given permission for private lessons.[29] Everett says, "There was, while I was a student, no provision made by the college for any instruction in any modern language but the French."[30]

There is, finally, no more convincing support for Ticknor's position than Andrew Peabody's well-known story of Follen's first class in German:

> German had never been taught in college before. . . . We knew of but two or three persons in New England who could read German; though there were probably many more, of whom we did not know. There were no German books in the bookstores . . . . There was no attainable classbook that could be used as a "Reader". A few copies of Noehden's Grammar were imported, and a few copies of I forget whose "Pocket Dictionary," fortunately too copious for an Anglo-saxon pocket. . . .[31]

It is against such a background that we must consider the accomplishment of translating (in 1814!) the whole of *Werther.*

3. *Ticknor and German Literature*

On October 14, 1815, Ticknor wrote to his friend Thomas Jefferson:

> With [Germany's] political organization and consequence, I believe we are sufficiently familiar in America, but its literature is a kind of *terra incognita* to us. Its language is so strangely different from all the foreign dialects we have been accustomed to learn, and their classical authors are all so recent, that it does not enter into the system of our education nor, until Mme. de Stael's book came among us, was its history or condition talked about or thought of.[32]

Ticknor then had been at Göttingen just over two months. The knowledge of German literature he brought from home had obviously been considerably supplemented, and he was in a good position to judge the state of things in America. His verdict is precisely the same as that in the passage from the *Life, Letters, and Journals* composed half a century later.[33]

Ticknor's appraisal of the condition of German literature in the United States is somewhat too stringent. If knowledge of German literature and of Goethe was not distinguished, it was at least on a higher level than purely linguistic attainments. By the very advantage of translation, German literature was in isolated cases familiar and in general far from unknown. It is unwise to assume from the presence of translations, even in more than one edition, that a given work was truly widespread, as the story of *Werther* in America itself attests. But the works of Gessner, Haller, Gellert, Winckelmann, Lavater, Klopstock, and Schiller, for example, circulated to some extent and their traces are to be found in the library catalogues and bookseller's lists of the time.[34]

Secondary sources were of moderate importance. Riesbeck's *Briefe,* as well as Burney's *Present State of Music in Germany,* had a good deal to say about literature, and both were available in New England before Ticknor was born. Riesbeck mentioned Wieland and Goethe at Weimar. The reviews, articles, and translations of William Bentley evince a considerable acquaintance with German poetry and thought. The fact that Bentley's Goethe collection was below the level of the rest of his library is significant for our immediate purpose but detracts little from his great achievement.

Among Ticknor's famous contemporaries his closest friend, Everett, certainly knew of Herder, if only from Stuart of Andover. His sketch of his college life[35] mentions no interest in German writers, however, and it appears that his very active occupation with Goethe, Schiller, and Klopstock was almost entirely a product of the enormous labor of Göttingen. The extent and nature of Bancroft's reading is problematical.[36] Cogswell had read an English *Werther* before he went to Göttingen, though he knew little else of Goethe and apparently as little or less of other authors. Even Longfellow, still at his studies long after the publication of Everett's famous critique in the *North American Review* and Bancroft's 1824 article in the same magazine, dates his connection with German literature from his dinner with Ticknor in Boston on May 2, 1826. His actual acquaintance with authors and works stems from his German university years. The witness for the South, Calvert, who was to acknowledge Goethe and Schiller as his greatest preceptors, entered Frankfurt in 1823 "unmoved by emotion at being in the birthplace of Goethe. For, at this point in Calvert's career, Goethe was no more than a name."[37]

What these influential young scholars had achieved in the study of German literature is small. Beside it Ticknor's feat of translation is of itself a rather overwhelming accomplishment. But exploration in the field of German belles-lettres began at an even earlier period in Ticknor's life, and the nature of the essay is at the same time an index of the degree to which German literature, as distinguished from the language, was modestly favored in New England.

It has already been noted that Ticknor's review of Sotheby's translation of *Oberon* is the only German literary item on the agenda of the Anthology Society.[38] As such it is one of the landmarks of early New England occupation with German literature. The text of the review[39] appeared as Article 8 in the September 1810 number of the *Monthly Anthology and Boston Review.*[40] Ticknor's characteristic conservatism is reflected in his appraisal of Wieland: a man of "atrocious opinions ... fanaticism in youth to skepticism, jacobinism, etc. in his riper years." Of the poem his judgment is almost unreserved praise: ". . . amidst these occasional defects the spirit of poetry shines forth with surpassing splendour, and the Oberon, as a whole, exhibits an exuberance of imagination, unparalleled in modern poetry." In all the article there is no mention of the German text, other works of Wieland, or other German writers. (In 1816, when he gave Channing a reproachful lesson on German literature, we can see the effect of his new acquaintance with the original: ". . . if you had read . . . Wieland's Oberon,—even in Sotheby,—. . . you would not have said 'the Germans do not know how to tell stories.' "[41])

The isolated and almost transitory impression of this study is reasonably characteristic of contemporary interest in German literature. It was not founded on a wide and sure basis of familiarity. Each man, in so far as he was so inspired, struggled to build for himself some knowledge of an author, a work, or a whole field. The effort was only mildly contagious. Most of the structure disappeared with the man or with his own loss of interest and left little trace on his times. To be sure, some of Bentley's labor endured, though in so fragmentary a state that one mourns for the greater losses. The solid foundations were laid by the young men who studied in Europe in the early century, and Ticknor was first among them. How did his interest grow from its seemingly impermanent beginning?

4. *Ticknor, Goethe, and Werther*

"Ce qui est sans égal et sans pareil, c'est Werther: on voit là tout ce que le génie de Goëthe pouvoit produire quand il étoit passionné."[42]

If Ticknor in 1813 or 1814 read *De l'Allemagne* with anything like the attention he claims, he must have noted the frequent references throughout the book to the "representative of all German literature" and particularly the conspicuous place which *Werther* occupies in Mme. de Staël's consideration of Goethe and in her impression of his personality. Stimulated perhaps by such passages as the above, Ticknor turned to the study of Goethe and the reading of *Werther*.

Ticknor had apparently read *Werther* in English translation, as well as in German. We even know which version he used, for in his Göttingen notes[43] he quotes an article on *Werther* in the *Neue Bibliothek der schönen Wissenschaften*,[44] confirming "that our English was, as I have always suspected, a translation from the French."[45]

What other works of Goethe Ticknor read we shall probably never know. There is only one specific indication of wider reading and that is, by its nature, subject to a slight discount. Sartorius, writing a letter of introduction for Ticknor and Everett to take to Weimar, praises his American friends to Goethe: "Sie ...kennen Ihre Schriften besser, als viele Deutsche; diese letztern haben sie eben angetrieben, wie sie mir oft gesagt, nach Deutschland zu kommen."[46]   There is further support to be found in the journals and notebooks, though it is by implication. The journals are filled with allusions to Goethe and visits to *loca sancta*, before as well as after Göttingen. The eagerness with which he studied Goethe at Göttingen is of corroboratory significance.

Even a passing acquaintance with the ways of Ticknor's mind is virtual assurance that he read more than *Werther* and more than Goethe. In his letter to Jefferson of October 14, 1815, he gives his Virginia correspondent a disquisition on the freedom and expansion of German scholarship and a quick review of the status of the best authors. He mentions Goethe, Klopstock ("except for his odes . . . out of fashion"), Wieland, Bürger, Voss, Lessing, and Schiller. It is true that he might have picked up all this knowledge since August 4, when he arrived. We are relieved of doubt, however, by his statement: "From what I had read of their literature in America I was satisfied it was very extraordinary but my expectations have been much exceeded." Such an elusive remark would not count for much, if it were not for Ticknor's acknowledged distinction in the field of books and literature. Jefferson, whom he visited shortly after finishing his translation of *Werther*, praised him to John Adams as "the best bibliograph I have met with."[47]   It is very possible therefore that this evidence does not represent the maximum of his knowledge but only a brief indication of considerable reading.

Our concern is, in any case, primarily with Goethe and *Werther*. It is possible to treat the two almost in the same breath, since they were, for the period, nearly synonymous. Concerning the general American ignorance of Goethe at this time one of the earliest investigators wrote, "Aside from the Werther poems and criticisms . . . there is little Goethe material of note prior to 1812."[48]   The singular review of the *Wahlverwandtschaften* in the 1812 issue of Walsh's *American Review* still speaks of Goethe as "the well-known author of Werther and Charlotte,"[49] and the equation of the author with a single work was largely valid far beyond this time. Stuart Atkins, the most recent authority on *Werther*, says of Europe even into mid-century, "Since the time of Madame de Staël a select few had known of Goethe's other works."[50] The statement is no less true of America.[51]

The special fate of *Werther* has often been summarized.[52] For the period preceding Ticknor's translation the following statement by Long is pertinent:

> American enthusiasm for *Werther* had its vogue principally between the years 1784 and 1809 . . . when nine reprints in three different English translations, a dramatized version, several novels, and a score of poems, all related in one way or another to the subject, made their appearance in this country.[53]

This gives the situation in its most favorable light. Two of the three translations, for example, had extremely restricted circulation. Productions of the play were anything but frequent. There was only one which Ticknor could have seen.

It was during this period of early interest that the Malthus translation came to America, first in Philadelphia in 1784, again in New York in 1795. In 1807 came two other translations, those of Render and Pratt, neither of which, in this early day, rivalled the Malthus version in popularity. Certain of *Werther's* numerous progeny, like the *Letters of Charlotte*, and especially Reynold's play, *Werter*, appeared in America by the late 1790's. *Werter* was produced in Boston as late as 1809. Reviews, first reprints of English ones and later original discussions, also preceded Ticknor's translation.

These by-products of America's principal taste in German literature flourished in some extent and considerable diversity of quality until around 1806-1807. That period marks the end of the first flush of productive interest (as shown in translations and imitations), though the special attraction of the reading public lasted well into the century. It also marks the years of Ticknor's college studies at Dartmouth. His occupation at college, however, is not the only explanation for the fact that Ticknor apparently knew none of the secondary *Werther* items and only one of the translations. With the sole exception of the

Malthus text, these *Werther* items occupied a relatively inconspicuous place in the total literary life of the early Republic.

Frequent reference will be made to the three translations which reached this country. A brief biographical note on the respective authors will serve for further comparison with Ticknor.

The first English translation is ascribed to Daniel Malthus (1730-1800), father of the more famous Thomas Robert Malthus. Unfortunately the only specific evidence from first hand contradicts this. Long cites the letter which the younger Malthus wrote to the *Gentleman's Magazine* (one of the sources in identifying the translation), correcting the obituary notice where Daniel Malthus is "mentioned as the translator of some pieces from the German and the French. I can say from certain knowledge that he did not translate them."[54] There is no adequate indication who wrote the translation, if Malthus didn't, and it is usually referred to as the Malthus version. (B. Q. Morgan's *Bibliography of German Literature in English Translation* ascribes it to R. Graves.) In any case it is done from the generally reliable French of Phillippe-Charles Aubry, who was apparently assisted by a German, Woldemar Friedrich von Schmettau. Aubry's *Passions du jeune Werther*, naturally from Goethe's 1774 text, was published in 1777. The Malthus version appeared in 1779 and numerous times thereafter. The introduction is commendably honest about not using the German original, but a hint of the excision of certain "sentiments of religion [which] border upon extravagance" is a warning of grave maltreatment of the text.

Render, whose translation of 1801 was the first to use the 1787 text, was of German origin. He came to England around 1790 and taught German at various places, including Cambridge and Oxford. He wrote other translations (Kotzebue and Schiller) as well as grammatical texts. In his introduction and appendix he claims not only unusual linguistic competence but also special personal qualifications for translating this particular work. He was a close friend of Goethe, Charlotte, and Werther and had the extreme fortune of talking to Werther a few days before his death. At least so he says. Long leaves relatively little of his story intact.[55]

Samuel Jackson Pratt (1749-1814) was a prolific writer, especially of plays, many under the pseudonym of Courtney Melmoth. Most of his own production was to a wearisome degree sentimental and diffuse, qualities which, besides dubious linguistic attainments, characterize his version of *Werther*. His introduction is by contrast sober and respectful of the original. It betrays none of the moralizing suspicion with which *Werther* was frequently viewed, even by its translators. The date of the first edition of his translation is uncertain. The second appeared in 1809. Pratt worked with the 1787 version, though beginning with the "Editor to the Reader" he made predominant use of the 1774 version, a peculiarity shared in part by Render, who compounds the irregularity by stealing part of the text from Malthus.[56] By coincidence Ticknor's library of English books, now located at Dartmouth, contains two of Pratt's other works, *Gleanings Through Wales, Holland, and Westphalia* (London, 1795) and his *Observations on the Night Thoughts of Dr. Young* (London, 1776). The latter is a presentation copy from "Courtney Melmoth." Ironically there is inserted in it a holograph note identifying the author with an unprincipled young man, successively cleric, absconder, actor, and "writer for booksellers in town," who on his marriage in Dublin abandoned the name of Pratt in favor of his wife's name, Melmoth. All this is true. To the romantic pursuits of Pratt's earlier life may be added a venture in fortune-telling, his last before turning to writing. Many of his books were successful with the public if not with critics; several were translated into German.

5. *The Source of Ticknor's Original*

The Reverend John Sylvester John Gardiner, Rector of Trinity Church, prepared young men for Harvard and gave further instruction in Latin and Greek to those who had graduated. Ticknor studied under him for two or three years. He was uniquely favored among Gardiner's students by invitation to the supper circle, "always agreeable, perfectly simple and easy, full of fun and wit, and always rich in literary culture. It was my first introduction to such society."[57] At Gardiner's he met James Savage, Buckminster, James Ogilvie, and William Smith Shaw. Connection with the Anthology Society was automatic. Gardiner himself was President, Savage was Secretary, Buckminster was a charter member and Shaw was a member of the Superintending Committee, Treasurer of the Club, and most important for the matter at hand, founder of the Boston Athenaeum. From the Athenaeum, as we have seen, came Ticknor's—or rather Adams'—copy of *Werther*. It is hard to guess how long, without Shaw's help, Ticknor might have had to search Boston for a German original.

The translation of *Werther* is probably the matter with which Ticknor was, as he says in the basic passage of the *Life, Letters, and Journals*, "occupied through the summer and autumn of 1814." The last date on the manuscript is December 10, 1814, and by that time he was presumably through with Adams' book. The provenance of the book is interesting. Its further fate—or presumed fate—is no less so, though it is certainly less complimentary to Ticknor. Henry Adams says:

> Wishing to have a copy of Göthe's "Werther," he borrowed it from the John Quincy Adams library with the connivance of Shaw and never returned it, one more example in high quarters of what Charles Lamb termed the gentle art of book-keeping. . . . A footnote may be added to the "Werther" incident. In December, 1815, there was sold at auction in Boston a notable collection of books, sent to America by Ticknor. Lot 125 was Göthe's "Sorrows of Werther" in German, Frankfort, 1795.[58]

Henry Adams adds as a footnote to the above:

> There is a little doubt here on the sale of Ticknor's books. The *Life* says that his library was sold "when Mr. Ticknor went to Europe." He sailed in April, 1815, and the sale of books was in December. The catalogue has no name and the books were reported as having come from Europe. That they were Ticknor's is noted by John Pickering of Salem who followed closely the sales at auction. . . .

6. *Ticknor and Werther in Later Years*

One of the mysteries surrounding Ticknor's *Werter* is that he made no contemporary reference to it. For the original *Werther* he had an abiding affection, and it appears frequently on the pages of his notebooks and journals. Only in the curious interest Ticknor shows for "our English" version and the high scorn he expresses for it do we find any reflection of the months of assiduous and affectionate labor that went into his own translation. The passage cited from his Göttingen notes referring to the Malthus work is factual and impersonal compared to this remark from his letter to Jefferson of October 14, 1815 where the repressed flame of conscious superiority burns high: "*Werther,* which we know in English only by a miserable imitation of a garbled French translation, made by some one who understood neither of the languages . . . ."

Throughout Ticknor's journals *Werther* clearly occupies the place of most favored and honored book. The first appearance of Goethe is, by more than coincidence, a significant mention of *Werther.* On August 1, 1815, travelling just inside Prussia on his way to Göttingen, and on German soil for the first time, Ticknor found himself, on his birthday, lonesome in a dreary and battle-worn landscape and he says, ". . . it was in vain that I read in Werther and endeavoured to forget myself as I had often done before in my interest for him."[59]

The second Goethe reference in Ticknor's diaries is also to *Werther.* Before the opening of the regular semester on October 27, he took a brief trip to Hannover, and in the entry for September 20, 1815, he writes: "The evening we passed pleasantly enough at Hofrath Feder's with a small party, among whom were our old acquaintances Mad. Hayne and her daughter, and Mad. Kestner, Goethe's Charlotte."[60]

If the degree to which poor Frau Kestner occupied the attention of the Americans in Germany is any index of her situation in German society in general, she must have been one of the principal *Sehenswürdigkeiten* of the country. A year and a half later Cogswell wrote: "On my way here [Göttingen] from Frankfort I turned aside from the route to pass by Wezlar, and pluck a sprig or two from the lime trees, which shade the grave of the young Jerusalem, and, by a strange accident, I could have presented them to Charlotte two days afterward, as I was introduced to her in the library, the first day of my arrival here."[61]

Even the familiar record of Ticknor's visit with Goethe at Weimar is colored by his earlier acquaintance with the passionate work of Goethe's youth: ". . . his person is not only respectable but imposing, and yet I saw little in it that indicated the character he ascribes to his youth, little of the lover of . . . Charlotte and still less of the Author of . . . Werther . . ." He can picture Jean Paul's disappointment when he came "expecting to find in his conversation the characteristicks of Werther and Faust."[62]

Ticknor made his own pilgrimage to Wetzlar, inspired not

only by his affection for *Werther* but further by the visit to Goethe in October, 1816. On March 25, 1817, he had taken final leave of his friends of the Göttingen years and by the 27th he was in Marburg.

Here I parted from my friend . . . and for the first time, yesterday morning [March 28], commenced a journey in Europe *alone*. I soon entered Darmstadt and dined at Giessen. . . . The temptation was strong upon me to go a few miles out of my way and visit Wetzlar, not because the great tribunal before which German Princes were for centuries tried like common men here held its seat till everything was overturned in the great convulsion of 1805; but because this is the very valley where the whole scene of *Werther* was laid. The temptation was *so* strong I could not resist it. I went, then, though I had previously resolved not to go, bought me a *Werther* and took a guide and set off to see how much was history and how much imagination.

Before the Wildbacher Gate I instantly recognized the fountain which makes such a figure in the letters and once in *Hermann and Dorothea*, and then taking horses set off for Garben, a couple of miles distant, which is the Wahlheim of the Romance. On the way I imagined that we passed the valley where the scene between Werther and Charlotte's distracted lover happened, and the chilly wind which blew as we went through it gave me a sensation of sadness such as I have seldom felt. I was still quite alone. A little farther on, I mounted the rocks where Werther passed the dreadful night after he had left Charlotte, and in the village itself I needed no guide to show me the old church, the lime trees, the burying ground, and the village houses which he has described with such fidelity. On returning to the city I stopped again on the rocks, read the description of his despair and stayed until the parting sun had almost descended behind the hills. Then I hastened to Wetzlar and as a final farewell went a few moments to the Hibbal Gardens, which Goethe had in his recollections and fancy when he described the parting scene in the last letter of the first Book. I am, on the whole, glad I went. This cold and cheerless Spring has, indeed, saddened the valley in which Charlotte and Werther lived so thoughtlessly together; but still it is impressed in my memory as it is, and, as to the rest, even in its brightest and gayest form the scenery would have disappointed the expectations with which Goethe's poetical feeling had filled my imagination.[63]

There is no mention of *Werther* in the long period between Ticknor's European journeys. That his interest in the book was still vivid, after twenty years, is curiously documented by his numerous meetings during his second trip with young Kestner, "the Hanoverian Minister [in Rome], son of Werther's Albert and Charlotte."[64] On February 15, 1837, he writes:

> This evening Mr. Kestner, the Hanoverian minister, came to
> see us and brought with him a portfolio, containing about an hun-
> dred letters from Goethe to his father and mother, who are the
> Charlotte and Albert of *Werther's Sorrows*, together with some
> other papers and a preface of his own, the whole constituting a
> full explanation and history of that remarkable work. He read us,
> for a couple of hours, curious extracts from different parts of it
> and proposes to come again and read more. The principal points
> are these. Kestner was an agent of the Hannoverian Government
> at the Imperial *Kanzley* in Wetzlar, where he became affianced to
> Charlotte Buff, whose character and position in her father's family
> were like those of the lady in *Werther*, except that she had none
> of the false sentimentality of the romantick personage. Goethe
> came to Wetzlar in the latter part of 1772, remained there four
> months, fell in love with the lady, did not conceal his passion from
> any of the parties nor attempt to urge a suit, became however at
> last alarmed at his own position, and after much such a conversa-
> tion as occurs at the end of the first Book of *Werther* tore himself
> from Wetzlar without leave-taking and went to Frankfurt. About
> the same period, the younger Jerusalem fell in love with *another*
> lady at Wetzlar, borrowed Kestner's pistols by a note which I saw,
> and destroyed himself with *Emilia Galotti* open before him, just as
> is described in *Werther*. Goethe in 1774 made a romance of the
> two stories and sent Kestner and his wife the first copy. They
> were offended at the publicity given to what touched themselves,
> and at the colouring given to the character of Albert and the feel-
> ings of Charlotte. He promised to publish something that should
> set the matter right, but his success and fame prevented him, and
> he never kept his word. They, too, forbore further complaints
> and continued good friends with him, as appears from the long
> correspondence they kept up, extending from 1772 to 1791, besides
> a few more letters coming down to 1816. The best and most
> curious part of the matter, however, is the little notes and early
> letters of 1772, 3, and 4.[65]

This passage is quoted in full, not only because most of it has
not before been published, but because it furnishes a neat and
brief sketch of the background of *Werther*. What is common-
place to any present student of Goethe was, at least as far as
real documentation goes, fascinatingly new to Ticknor. It was
over 15 years later that the Kestner materials were finally published. (In Ticknor's library at Dartmouth is his copy of Kestner's book.) On February 17, Ticknor writes:

> Mr. Kestner came again this evening and read the rest of what
> I wanted to hear out of his portfolio of letters about Goethe,
> Werther, etc. It was very curious and interesting. The fact

seems to be that, in the first book of Werther's Letters, Werther is undoubtedly Goethe himself, Charlotte is Charlotte Buff, and Albert is Kestner, and much of what is described there really passed. In the second book, Werther is undoubtedly the Young Jerusalem, who was a Secretary of Legation and met the affronts there described and whose death and last days are described often word for word in *Werther*, from a letter sent by Kestner to Goethe. So, too, Charlotte is undoubtedly the lady Young Jerusalem was in love with, but Albert was hardly worth changing and remains the same. Yet still through the whole of the second Part there are many traits and touches, like all that relates to the Profile, that belong essentially to Kestner and Charlotte Buff.[66]

In 1870, one year before his death, Ticknor makes his last mention of *Werther*. He is annotating the journal entry of 1817, which concerns his pilgrimage to Wetzlar. Over 50 years after that sentimental journey and over 30 years after his last close personal touch with Goethe's work he looks back at the translation with which, in effect, he started his career as a scholar in belles-lettres: "...and I have ever since had a great attachment to that book."[67] This is the last testimony to an active interest which spanned the whole of Ticknor's productive lifetime.

From the biographical point of view the most persistent—and most elusive—question in this chapter of Ticknor's life is: Why, with his strict Puritan background and his congenial classical training, did Ticknor find such lasting fascination in Goethe's *Werther*? Without doubt he devoted more time, effort, and affection to it than to any other reading of his early years. Yet we are almost shocked by the contrast between the character of Ticknor as we generally know him and the subterranean pressures and emotional stresses of Werther's disintegrating personality. Ticknor, according to the accepted view and by witness of his best known writings, was self-possessed, calm, enthusiastic but not excited, socially gracious, dignified, assured, and unperplexed by doubt—the antithesis of Werther. Yet somewhere there must be an area of similarity and affinity. Part of it is defined when we realize that this work of translation reflected and satisfied an urge for literary creation of which there is hardly a trace in his other works. Here he is much like Adams, in whose case, however, we have express statement of a strong desire to live as an author. And if Ticknor read Malthus before the fall of 1814, which is very possible, his translation may reflect a laudable desire to see justice done to a masterpiece of literature. But the particular choice of *Werther* remains puzzling.

Harry Maync said of Goethe: "Er entringt sich der Tragik durch die Tragödie." If an author escapes tragic consequences by the writing of tragedy may not the close scrutiny of tragedy fulfill for the translator an analogous function in diminished degree? In the general view of Ticknor's character this suggestion does not seem promising. But the published letters and diaries are fragmentary. The question must therefore take this form: Is there in Ticknor a hitherto unexplored vein of melancholy or even an occasional approach to despair, for which *Werther* provided both sympathetic understanding, so to speak, and an avenue of escape? To a considerable extent concrete proof is unlikely, for Ticknor knew how and for whom he cared to write, and he did not have a policy of revealing his intimate soul. Yet out of his manuscript journals there comes an occasional surprising voice, the sound of which is oddly familiar. One or two instances appear in the *Werther* references themselves (see above). There is a striking passage in the journals for 1816, the only entry in a period of nearly six months, which is more eloquent:

> April 8. Mr. and Mrs. Perkins arrived here the 28th ult. and remained till three days ago. We then accompanied them to Cassel and parted from them yesterday morning with a bitterness of regret which is hardly compensated by the happiness which their visit gave me. Two days have since passed away, and every thing in Göttingen has become absolutely distasteful to me from a kind and degree of homesickness which I have not before felt in Europe. Whether I shall entirely overcome these impressions and be again as contented here as I have been, I know not, but of this I am sure, that the recollection of the last short and happy week will never return to my memory without bringing at the same time a sense of desolation such as I have not known since I felt the shock of the vessel as it finally parted from the wharf a year ago and separated me, perhaps forever, from my home. I know that I now write in a moment of unusual and even unnatural depression and I feel that the sensation of the loss I have suffered makes me ungrateful for the happiness I have just enjoyed, but still I do not think that I could desire to meet Mrs. Perkins again to be again separated from her. Indeed—indeed—I never felt so entirely alone in the world—so forsaken—as in the two days which have just passed, and I can hardly imagine a form of happiness which I could wish to purchase at so dear a price.[68]

(The Perkinses of this passage had long been known to Ticknor. Among his best friends in Boston were the elder and younger Perkinses and the Higginsons. Ticknor, Everett, Haven, and the Perkinses crossed the Atlantic together. Barbara Higginson Perkins was of extraordinary beauty. Talleyrand remembered "Barbe" as one of the loveliest young women he had ever seen.)[69]

From the period previous to his trip to Europe there is little in the way of purely personal material and certainly nothing like the above. So it is impossible to document Ticknor's mood at the time of his first reading of *Werther* and during the translating. There seems, incidentally, to be no question of a burning love in Ticknor's young life. Yet the manuscript journals contain, in passages like the Perkins entry and the *Werther* descriptions, suggestions of smouldering melancholy which goes beyond simple nostalgia, and in his youthful sketches and the early landscape impressions of the European journey there is evidence of a love of nature, in kind not unlike Goethe's. In such directions may lie the way to an understanding of Ticknor's love for *Werther*.

7. *Scholarly Interest in Werther*

From a small but impressive manuscript volume of study notes made at Göttingen and never before published comes notable proof that *Werther* was the object not only of Ticknor's literary delectation but of his scholarly attention as well. The notes are remarkably copious and detailed. The knowledge, indeed the technique, which they reveal was, in the field of contemporary literature, the property of few other Americans of the time.

Ticknor's writing is always original and individual. The style of the future historian of letters is already developing. The several sections, unless otherwise noted, are given in full and as numbered in the untitled volume from which they are drawn. Only the punctuation is edited.

1. A great deal has been said about the moral tendency of Werter's letters. Mad. de Stael says in *Germany* Part—chap.—[70] that they have occasioned many self-murders. So it was said that Schiller's *Robbers* had turned the heads of some of the students in the German universities and I rested the two stories on the same foun-

dation, until I found Arenswald's letters.[71] These were published
at Franckfort and Leipsic in 1782 (pp. 56) and a review of them
may be found in Henry Maty's *New Review* for 1783, vol. 4, p. 276.
Arenswald was a captain in the German service and seems to have
been in character something like the imaginary Werther. He trusted
his fortune to a faithless friend and destroyed himself on account
of its loss 29 Sept., 1781. The editor of his letters says that his
tedium vitae was, in some measure, brought on by reading *Werther*
and adds an instance of a young man whose mistress had married
another and who was soon after found dead in his chamber with the
Sorrows of Werther in his hand.

2. The *Sorrows of Werther* were first published in 1774, Lipz.,
1. 8 vo. Another edition appeared in 1775, Lipz.[72] and a third with
additions, Berlin, divided into two parts ["2. 8vo." crossed out. Ed.],
1778.[73] It was translated into French by B.S. de S. ["Seckendorf,
Barbier[74] 17199" added. Ed.], 1776[75]; by d'Yverdun with a critical
examination of the Wertheriana, Paris, 1776.[76]; another anonymous
translation by D'Aubry with a discourse on German Litterat. by
Count Schmettau, Manh. and Par., 1. 8vo., 1777; also one by . . .
[Illegible. Ed.] de la Bedoyère,[77] 1804, Barbier 19537. The last letters to Charlotte are imitated in Count Hartig's Melanges de Prose
et de Vers,[78] Paris, 1788. It was translated into English in 1779,[79]
and parts of it were published in verse by Amelia Pickering, Lond.,
1788.[80] Into Italian by Caj.[81] Grassi with a defense of the work,
Poschiavo, 1782; and by C. Ludger, London, 1788, 2. 12mo. Into
Swedish, anon.,[82] 1783, 8vo; and Russian by Kyriak, Petersburg,
17*[83], 1. 8vo. It produced a great sensation in Germany, when it
first appeared, and was followed by a crowd of imitations and criticisms, etc., etc. Among them the most remarkable seem to have been
the following: *Freuden des Jungen Werthers—Leiden und Freuden
von Werthers des Mannes* [Sic. Ed.] (by Frederick Nicolai), Berlin, 1775, 8vo.[84] *Etwas über die Leiden und Freuden des Jungen
Werthers,*[85] Dresden, 1775, 8vo. (by Christian Aug. Bertram).
Gespräche über die Leiden des Jungen Werthers, Berlin, 1775, 8vo.
(by Reibe[86]). *Das Wertherfieber, ein unvollendetes Familien-
stück,* Leipz., 1776, 8vo. (This is a pungent satire. In Meusel's
Gelehrten Deutschlands, Nachtr. I., 4th edit., p. 206, E.A.A. von
Geshen[87] is said to be the author; but in the *Hallischen Gelehrten
Zeitung,* 1776,[88] it is changed to a B.V.J.). *Masuren oder der Junge
Werther,* Frank Lipz., 1775 (by Aug. Fred. von Goue). *Mordgeschichte vom Jungen Werther, Romanze,* 1776, 1. 8vo.[89] *Die Leiden
des Jungen Werther,*[90] *Trauerspiel,* Bern, 1776, 8vo. *Die Leiden
der Jungen Wertherinn,* Eisen., 1776, 8vo. (by Aug. Cor. Stock-
mann). *Werther ein Bürgerliches Trauerspiel,* Frank. Leipz.,
1777.[91] (by ——Willer). The best criticism upon it is to be found,
I understand, in Engel's Letters upon it in the *Philosophen für
die Welt.*[92]

3. Küttner, in his *Charaktere Deutscher Dichter und Prosaisten* published at Berlin without his name in 1781, speaks thus first of Goethe's earlier pieces—and then of *Werther*, p. 514 [There follows a long quote on the impact of Goethe's early works, however undisciplined, and on the emotional current which sweeps the reader through the tribulations of Werther, with a counterblast at those who find suicide defended or character overdrawn. Ed.]

4. "Klopstock und Lessing stiegen noch in Ansehen, weil Werthers Lotte bei dem schönen Gewitter, Klopstock! ausgerufen hatte, und auf Werthers Pulte, als man den melancholischen Schwärmer in seinem Blute fand, Lessings Emilia Galotti aufgeschlagen lag." *Fragmente uber den Geist der Deutchen Litteratur*, published in the *Bibliothek der Redenden und Bildenden Kunste* [Sic. Ed.] IV. Band, 121. Seite, ann. 1807.

5. Prof. Benecke told me that when *Werther* first appeared it was so much the fashion, that many young men dressed themselves in a blue coat and yellow waistcoat and small clothes, such as Werther's dress is described in his letter of Sep. 6., P. II, and at the conclusion, after his death, and such as young Jerusalem's dress always was; for this part of the picture is historical. See *Aus Meinem Leben*, Buch XII.

6. For some very good remarks on Werther see *Neue Bib. d. schönen Wissensch.*,[93] Tom LXX, p. 132 sq. and a long review of it in the same work Vol. XVIII, p. 46 sq. That our English was, as I have always suspected, a translation from the French, see *ibid.*, XXXII, 144.

7. [This section contains more than 20 detailed collations of passages in *Werther* with their counterparts or sources in *Dichtung und Wahrheit*, as well as miscellaneous identifications.) He finds "the principal passages . . . on the story of Werther" to be in Book 12 and Book 13, specifically pp. 231-238 and pp. 341 360. He notes many small but significant points of resemblance, as, for example, when he comments on *Werther*, Book I, July 30 and compares "the pride of Albert that Werther loved Charlotte, with the following opinion (III, 11, p. 20) : 'Die reinste Freude, die man an einer geliebten Person finden kann, ist die, zu sehen dasz sie andere erfreut.' " Ticknor's pagination for *Dichtung und Wahrheit* is of course from the first edition (Tübingen: Cotta, 1811-14).]

8. The ode of Klopstock to wh. Charlotte alluded at the end of the letter of June 16 is the beautiful one written in 1759 and called "Frühlingsfeyer." The verses intended more particularly than any other must be the 7 last, tho' to give it its full effect, the associations should extend to the whole piece. This Ode was the great favourite of Coleridge when he studied, or rather when he lounged away his time, at Göttingen. Apropos, it may be well to remember that his tragedy, wh. he published only 3 years since, was chiefly written here before his talents were perverted, and thus its merit may be accounted for.

The last remarks are included not only for their obvious interest in another field but for the equally obvious personal resentment at Coleridge's lassitude. The surprising knowledge represented by the above passages was purchased by a regimen of unceasing application to study. If Ticknor's scholarly breadth was unparalleled in the America of his day, his tireless energy was nearly as extraordinary. He spent, by plan, 12 to 13 hours a day at his work, habitually rising at five to start with his Greek. In his first semester he missed one class. After that he missed none. In Göttingen Ticknor and Everett were commonly and with good-humored respect known as the "Doctor" and the "Professor". More than one later American visitor to Europe found that, wherever these two had been before him, continental regard for American learning had soared.

8. *The Text of Ticknor's Translation*

Internal description of the manuscript is quickly accomplished. Adams' edition of *Werther* was the 1787 text. Of this text Ticknor, like most of his predecessors, left out a large part of the long Ossian passage. Otherwise his only suppression of the original is the latter part of Part II, September 4, where, instead of finishing the story of the unhappy farm-hand, he simply places four asterisks after "nobody knows what has become of him," and proceeds to the next letter. What he would have done in the event of publication is conjectural. He finishes the story of the farm-hand in the section entitled "The Editor to the Reader." Hence he apparently had nothing against it on moral grounds. With the exceptions noted Ticknor left out nothing of consequence. What is more he does not share his predecessors' penchant for adding to Goethe's text. His translation is therefore as nearly complete as the best and better than most of the early versions, two of which were not even from the German and all seven of which may fairly be said to present a mutilated text. And it must be remembered that Ticknor did not make final preparations for publication.

The manuscript gives little indication of his ultimate intentions. The dates on the title page and the three footnotes (and one "insert" instruction) are the only words in the book which are not from Goethe's *Werther*. Ticknor left the manuscript, in effect, ready for editing. But he never referred in any way to publishing the work, unless the last words of the mysterious sentence, "I got so far as to write a translation of 'Werther,' but no farther," are to be taken in that sense. The presence of the footnotes is not decisive, because Ticknor annotated everything including his notebooks.

It is a misfortune for American letters that Ticknor did not publish the result of his careful labor and absorbing interest. What would have been the effect on our early interest in *Werther* and in Goethe, had there appeared, in 1814 or 1819, a truly worthy version by a well-known American? Edward Everett, one of the few who saw the manuscript before its disappearance, was greatly impressed by it. Many scholars have since speculated on the whereabouts and the nature of the translation. Its rediscovery confirms entirely the words of a scholar who wrote a century and a quarter later, when the work was still presumed lost: ". . . if it had been presented to the public, (it) would have been an interesting contribution to *Werther* history, and doubtless a credit to American scholarship."[94]

The Sorrows of Young Werter

Nov. 23-Dec. 10, 1814

The Sorrows of Young Werter
Book First

TO THE READER.

I have collected with care whatever I could find of the story of the unfortunate Werter and now lay it before you, sure that I shall receive your gratitude for it. You cannot refuse your admiration to his talents, your love to his character, or your tears to his fate.

And you who have a soul of sensibility, you who suffer like him, draw consolation from his sorrows and take this little book for your friend, if fortune or your own errors deny you a better.

I am very glad that I am not with you. What a heart, my dear friend, has man! To leave you—*you* whom I love so much and from whom I was inseparable, and yet to be *glad*! But you forgive me for it, I know you do!

Have not my former attachments been exactly arranged by fortune to afflict a heart like mine? Poor Leonora! And yet, I am guiltless. Was I to blame that, while I was attracted and amused with the charms of her sister, a passion was springing up in her heart? And yet—am I entirely innocent? Did I not encourage her tenderness? Did I not trifle with the simple expressions of her unsophisticated feelings, which so often amused us, little as they were fit subjects for our amusement. Did I not—but why should man thus make his own misery? I *will*, my dear friend, grow better; I promise you I will. 1 will not continually brood over the little evil which fortune has cast upon me, as I always have done—I will enjoy the present, and the past shall be indeed gone by.

You are certainly right, my dear friend, the sorrows of mankind would be much fewer if they did not—Heaven knows why they are made so!—if they did not employ themselves with such an ingenuity of imagination in reviving past calamities rather than in improving the quiet of the present moment.

Be so good as to tell my mother that I will attend to her affairs to the best of my power and write to her about them immediately. I have spoken to my aunt and did not find her by any means the perverse woman she has been represented to me. She is open and lively and has an excellent heart. I explained to her my mother's complaints in relation to her part of the estate, and she explained to me her own pretensions and motives and the conditions on which she will be ready to give up all we ask and even more. In short, I cannot now write about it, but tell my mother that it is all going on very well. And I, my dear friend, have found new proof in this trifling affair that misunderstanding and mistake are the cause, perhaps, of more mischief in the world than cunning and malice. At any rate, instances of the last are much less frequent.

I am very pleasantly situated here. The solitude of this earthly paradise is the kindest balsam to my spirit, and the opening promise of Spring fills with unwonted warmth a heart which has been so often chilled. Every tree, every shrub is but a bouquet of flowers, and you might almost wish yourself changed to a May-bee, that you might float in the ocean of sweets and find all your nourishment there.

The town itself is unpleasant, but Nature is inexpressibly beautiful in its environs. It was this which induced the Marquis of ——— to form his garden on one of the hills, which here intersect each other in all directions and subside into the most beautiful vallies. The grounds are simple, and the moment you enter them you feel sure that the plan was not dictated by a professed gardner but by a feeling heart, which looked here only for its own enjoyment. I have already paid the tribute of my tears to the memory of the departed owner, amidst the ruins of an arbour, which was once his favourite resort and is now mine. I shall soon be master of the garden, for I gained the gardner's good will two days ago, and he shall not be a loser by it.

May 10

A magical calmness has taken possession of my faculties, like the serenity of the spring morning in which my whole heart is now rejoicing. I am alone, and find a genuine enjoyment of life amidst scenery like this, which seems to have been formed expressly for a spirit like mine. I am so happy, my dear friend, so completely absorbed in the enjoyment of mere existence, that my talents are suffering from it. I have lost all power to paint, and yet I never had more of an artists' talent than at this moment. When the refreshing dampness of the valley descends around me—when the noon-day sun pours his unavailing beams on the impenetrable shades of my chosen wood, and only an occasional solitary ray pierces to its inmost recess—when I rest myself among the high grass by the waterfall—and thus brought nearer to the earth find there a thousand wonderful varieties of vegetation—when I feel myself grow familiar and intimate with the untold tribes of the insect world that inhabit the plants around me and with the unnumbered and innumerable forms of those that creep and those that fly, and thus feel the sensible presence of that Almighty being, who formed us in his own image, the very breath of that Eternal being, who supports and preserves us in perpetual delight—O, my dear friend, when this bright vision dawns on my senses, and the world and the heaven I have imagined descend and rest in my soul—then, in fervent aspiration, I often commune with myself and ask: Canst thou recall that impression? Canst thou breathe that spirit upon thy canvass, which lives and glows within thee, and make that canvass the mirror of thy soul, as thy soul is the mirror of the Everlasting God? —O my friend! I bow to the earth and sink under the power and majesty of the conception!

May 12

I know not whether the country round here is lighted up by magick or whether I take the glowing picture from my own imagination, that the scenery about me seems so much like Paradise. There is, just out of the town, a fountain to which I am as much bound and enchanted as Melusina and her sisters. You descend a little hill to the entrance of a cave and are there led down twenty steps at the bottom of which the purest water gushes from a marble rock. The little wall, which forms the margin of the fountain, the lofty trees which cover the grounds about it, the coolness of the place—every thing is touching and impressive. Not a day passes in which I do not sit an hour there. The servant-girls come from the town to fetch water—an innocent and useful employment, which once occupied even the daughters of princes. While I am there, the vision of the days of the patriarchs rises in such power before me that I see our forefathers forming treaties and friendships, and the spirits of the blest hovering over the springs and fountains. O! he can never have refreshed himself with the coolness of a spring after a weary summer's walk, who cannot imagine all this!

May 13

You ask whether you shall send my books? For heaven's sake, my dear friend, keep them at home! I do not wish to be again led and excited and inflamed. My heart preys enough upon itself—I need only a little poetry to soothe me and this I find in all its perfection in my Homer. Many a time I have thus sobered my boiling blood, and truly nothing was ever so unequal and unsettled as this heart. But I need not say this to you, my dear friend, *you*, who have so often mourned to see me rush from composure to extravagance—from mild melancholy to furious passion. My heart is like a sick child and therefore I give it its way in every thing. Don't tell any body so, however, for there are people who would blame me for it.

May 15

The common people of the town and especially the children have already learned to love me. When I first attempted to become acquainted with them and asked them in a familiar tone about this and that, some of them thought I intended to insult them and answered me abruptly. However, I did not suffer this to discourage me. I only found in it a strong confirmation of what I had often remarked before: that people will always find themselves removed to a chilling distance from the vulgar exactly in proportion to the degradation they think they shall suffer by condescension, and there are, besides, thoughtless people and writings, who will at one time descend to their inferiors in order to make their elevation the more obvious at other times.

I know very well that we are not and cannot all be equal, but I also know that he who thinks it necessary to retire from those whom he calls the vulgar in order to secure their respect is as contemptible as a coward who hides himself from his enemy because he is afraid to meet him.

Last evening I went to the fountain and found there a servant girl, who had left her pail upon the lowest step and was looking round for some of her companions to come and help her lift it to her head. I went down and spoke to her—"Shall I help you, my dear?" said I. She blushed like crimson. "O no Sir," said she. "No ceremony"—She took up her pail at once, and I helped her. She thanked me and disappeared.

May 17

I have made all sorts of acquaintances but have, as yet, found no companions. I know not what there is in me so attractive, but the people here are so anxious to serve me and express so much good will towards me, that I am really sorry we have little in common and that I can make them only so imperfect a return. If you should ask me what sort of people they are here, I could only answer, such as you may find every where. Mankind are always a crude compound. Most of them are compelled to labour the greater part of their time for mere subsistence, and the little liberty which remains to them is so irksome, that they devise every possible means to get rid of it. Such is the destiny of man!

However, they are very worthy people. When I can forget

myself—when I can enjoy among them those common pleasures which are still spared to us—when I can partake the frank and sincere hilarity of their table, or join them in a walk, a dance or any such amusement, I find myself much the better for it; but then I must not allow myself to think of the talents that sleep and rust within me unused, and which, at such times, I am obliged carefully to conceal. The recollection of this is always painful to me, and yet to be misunderstood is the fate of all men like me.

Would to God that the friend of my youth were yet alive or that I had never known her! It is, perhaps, a weakness to desire what we can never enjoy; but still I cannot choose but feel that I have once possessed her, have once felt the intimate influence of that heart and those high talents, in whose presence I seemed to rise above myself, because then only I was all I was destined to be. Was any faculty of my mind then inactive? Could I not pour out before her all that mysterious enthusiasm with which nature has bound up my heart? Was not our intercourse a perpetual flow of taste and talent, whose varieties, even in trifles, bore every where the impress of genius? And now—! Alas! thy riper years led thee, indeed, soonest to the tomb; but never can I forget thee, never can I forget thy active talents or thy heavenly disposition!

A few days ago I met a Mr. V———, a frank young man with a promising physiognomy. He has just come from College and is not, perhaps, vain, tho' he thinks he knows a good deal more than those around him. Indeed, you see at the first blush that he has been industrious and has accumulated quite a pretty little stock of knowledge. As soon as he heard that I could paint and read Greek (two prodigies here in the interior) he came to see me and unfolded a deal of learning from Batteux to Wood—and from De Piles to Winkelmann—assured me he had read the whole of the first part of Sulzer's Theory and had now in his possession a manuscript of Dr. Heyne on the study of Antiquity. I liked all this very well.

I have also become acquainted with a man of sterling worth and of an open and honest heart—the Prince's Steward. I am told that it is a genuine pleasure to see him surrounded with his nine children; and, above all, report speaks goldenly of his eldest daughter. He has invited me to his house, and I shall take the first opportunity to visit him. He lives at a royal hunting-lodge about a league and an half from here, where he has had permission to reside since his wife's death rather than at the Steward's House in town, which can now only renew the recollection of his sorrows.

I have besides been annoyed by a few absurd people, in whom every thing is troublesome, but nothing so intolerable as the proofs and assurances of their friendship.

Farewell. This letter, at least, will please you, for it contains nothing but plain matters of fact.

May 22

It has often been said that the life of man is but a dream, but I am continually reminded and persuaded of its truth. When I see the narrow limits within which the active and subtle faculties of man are constrained—when I see that all exertion is put forth only to satisfy the eagerness of desires which have no better object than to prolong our miserable existence—and that all our curious inquiries about certain points of doubtful disputation tend only to produce a false resignation, in which we amuse ourselves with covering the walls of our prison with gay forms and gilded landscapes—when I think of all this, my dear William, I am lost in astonishment—I retreat into my own bosom and find there a world, indeed, but what a world—more of dark vision and deceitful promise than of truth or reality—in short, I find every thing unsubstantial there also, and rush gaily forward dreaming like the rest.

That children are ignorant of the motives which determine their will is a point on which all philosophy is agreed; but that the great children, too, wander through the world, ignorant whence they come and whither they they are going, as little occupied with substantial pursuits and as much governed by cakes and pies and rods—this no man will believe and yet it seems as obvious as the noon-day sun.

I know very well what you will answer to all this, and I am willing to acknowledge that they are the happiest, who, like children, live only in the present, occupy themselves only in dressing and undressing their dolls and in gliding with respectful anxiety round the closet, in which mama has locked up the sweetmeats, and when, at last, they obtain the prize, swallow it with greedy haste and cry for more. This, I acknowledge, is happiness. They, too, are happy who give gawdy titles to their follies and perhaps their passions, and then present themselves to the world as the patrons of its improvements and happiness. They, too, are happy! But he who knows his own weakness, and can discern consequences in their causes—he who sees how eagerly the overgorged citizen labours to make his garden a paradise— with what alacrity the child of misfortune presses forward with his burthen—and how anxiously and equally all strive to pro- tract, even for one poor moment, their enjoyment of the light of the sun—he who sees all this is contented, too, and builds for himself a world in his own imagination—and *he,* too, is happy, for he is a man. However he may be oppressed, he still feels within himself the fervent love of freedom and the assurance that the escape from his thraldom is always within his own choice.

May 26

You have long known my attachment to particular places and disposition to build a tabernacle in retirement and then to settle down in its enjoyment. Well, here too I have found a spot which has already become dear to me.

About a league from the town is a place called Walheim. Its site on a hill is very beautiful, and if you go by the foot- path you have a view of the whole valley at once. A good hostess, who is cheerful and gay even in the wane of life, sells wine and beer and coffee—and, what is an attraction above all others, there are two lime-trees whose broad branches cast their shade on the little church green which is surrounded with fields and barns and cottages. I have very seldom found a spot so retired and solitary, and here I have planted my table and chair— drink my coffee and read my Homer. The first time accident led me under these lime-trees it was a clear noon and I found the place a perfect solitude. Every body was in the fields except a boy about four years old, who was sitting on the ground and held another about six months old between his feet before him with his arms round his little breast so as to serve as a sort of chair for him, and except the activity which sparkled in his dark eyes, he sat so still that you might have mistaken him for a statue. The scene struck me. I sat down upon a plough which stood there and eagerly copied this picture of fraternal affec- tion. I added part of the hedge, a barn-door, and some broken cart-wheels exactly as they stood before me, and found, at the end of an hour, that I had sketched a regular and interesting landscape, without having borrowed any thing from invention.

This confirmed my resolution to copy hereafter entirely from nature, for there only is inexhaustible wealth, and there only can a great artist be formed. The same arguments may be urged in favour of subjection to rules which are urged in favour of city manners. A man who is formed on them will, it is true, never produce any thing that will offend your taste or be absolutely disgusting, just as he who has been disciplined by the rules and proprieties of society can never be a bad neighbour or citizen; but still, after all that can be urged in their favour, these rules war against the original susceptibilities and perceptions of our nature.— Do you say I go too far—that they only restrain and prune the luxuriance of the vine, etc. etc.? My dear friend, will you indulge me in a comparison? It is with this as it is with love. An unpractised heart is completely dependent on the object of his affections, devotes all his time to her, wastes his faculties and his fortune only to persuade her anew every moment that he lives only in her. And now comes a grave philosopher, a man, if you please, in some publick employment, and says to him: "My dear Sir, to be in love is, indeed, manly; but then you should love like a man. Divide your time— give a part of it to labour and let your visits to your mistress be your relaxation and reward. Calculate your income, and when your necessary wants are satisfied, I would not forbid you to make her a present, but not so often—do it only on her birth day or some such anniversary." The young man follows the advice and becomes a very respectable, useful young man—nay, he is such an one as I would advise a prince to place high in his favour—but as for his love, it is gone, or if he is an artist, so is his talent. O, why does not the flood of genius oftener burst the banks that constrain it and astonish us with its fearful strength? It is because the sons of regularity and form have occupied those banks, whose houses and fields and flower-gardens would be laid waste, if policy had not taught them to erect mounds and dig canals to controul and divert the coming danger.

May 27

I see that I have fallen into apostrophes and similitudes and declamation and forgotten to tell you what finally became of the children. Well then, for about two hours I remained seated on my plough and lost in that reverie on painting of which you had several fragments in my yesterday's letter. Just before

sundown, a young woman came running towards the children—
who had not stirred all this time—with a basket on her arm
and long before she reached them, cried out: "You are a good
boy, Philip!" She curtsied to me and I returned her civility
and went up to her and asked her if she was the mother of the
children? She said she was, and while she gave the eldest half
a biscuit, took the youngest in her arms and kissed it with all
a mother's affection.

"I gave the youngest to Philip to hold," said she, "while
I went with the eldest into the village to buy some white-bread,
and sugar, and an earthen porridge pot."—I saw them all in
the basket, whose cover had fallen off—"I wanted to make some
porridge this evening for John" (that was the name of the
youngest) "but that rogue" (meaning the largest) "broke the
porridge-pot yesterday, while he was quarrelling with Philip
for the bread at the bottom." I asked after the eldest, and she
had hardly time to tell me he was driving a couple of geese
from the meadow, when he came running up and brought with
him a hazle-rod for the second. I continued my conversation with
the mother and found she was the school-master's daughter and
that her husband had gone to Switzerland in order to obtain
the estate of a deceased relation. "They have tried to cheat
him out of it," she said, "and would not answer his letters. So
he has gone himself, and God grant no accident may have
happened to him, for I have not heard a word from him since he
went away." I could hardly leave her, but I gave a creuzer to
each of the children and one to the mother herself to buy a
biscuit for the little one's porridge the next time she goes to
the village, and then we parted.

If all my faculties were unsettled and confused, the tumult
would be instantly appeased by the sight of a being like this
who moves with such happy tranquillity round the narrow
circle to which she is confined—never looks beyond the present
day—and is reminded by the falling leaves of autumn of nothing but the approach of winter.

Since this, I have been there very often and the children
have grown quite intimate with me. They come for their piece
of sugar when I drink coffee, and at evening I divide with
them my bread and butter and my whey. Sunday never fails to
bring them their creuzer, for if I am absent my hostess has orders to give it to them.

I have entirely won their confidence. They tell me all their affairs, and I find a great deal of amusement in their simple accounts of the passions and troubles of the village play-ground.

It has cost me a good deal to prevent their mother from "taking care that they don't trouble the gentleman."

May 30

What I said to you the other day of painting may be also said of poetry. It is only necessary that a man should have a natural perception of the beautiful and a power of expressing his feelings and then he is a poet. I have had an adventure to-day, which, if it were well described would make the most beautiful idyl in the world. But why should I talk of adventures —and idyls—and poetry? Must we still go on in the beaten foot-way, when we wish to speak the language of nature and passion?

If you expect any thing elevated and imposing from this prologue, you will be again miserably disappointed, for, after all, it is but a simple country-boy who has raised all this interest in me. I shall tell my story very ill, as I always do, and you will, I suppose, as usual reproach me with it. —It is still Walheim and nothing but Walheim that is so prolifick in extraordinary adventures.

There was a party from there under the lime-trees drinking coffee, and as they were not exactly to my fancy, I stopped under a shade farther back. A peasant came out from a neighbouring house and began to adjust the plough which I sketched a few days ago. His looks pleased me and therefore I spoke to him and inquired a little about his situation. We were soon acquainted and, as often happens with such sort of people, soon intimate. He told me that he was at service with a widow, and was very kindly treated by her. He said so much about her and praised her so much that I very soon saw he had more than a common regard for her. "She is not young," said he. "She was not well treated by her husband, and refuses to be married again" —and then he went on to place her in so interesting a light, spoke so much of her beauty and attractions, told me with such earnest sincerity how much he wished she would suffer him to remove the impression left by her former husband's perversity that I should be obliged to repeat to you word for word what he said if I were to attempt to give you an idea of the purity and sincerity of his affection. Nay, I must have the high gifts of genius and poetry to make you feel the earnestness of his manner, the tenderness of his voice, or the expression of his countenance. Language is too poor to convey to you the touching delicacy which was revealed in every tone and movement, and all I can do to recall it is flat and unprofitable. He was especially anxious that I should not suspect the purity of his affection or her character. My heart bears him witness, though my pen cannot express the passion with which he spoke of her person, which, though it had lost the charms of youth, had yet such power over him. Never did I meet or imagine an attachment at once so passionate and so pure. Do not smile when I tell you that the memory of such innocence and sincerity has penetrated to the bottom of my heart —that the picture of this delicate affection pursues me wherever I go, and that I seem myself almost infected and consumed with his passion.

I shall go and see her as soon as possible—or rather, upon second thought, I will avoid her. It is better that I should see only with the eyes of her lover, for perhaps if I were to see her myself, she might lose her attractions—and why should I destroy the beautiful picture of my own imagination?

June 16

Why do I not write to you? Are you a man of penetration and yet ask such a question? You ought to have known from instinct that I am not sick but that—in short, to come to the point at once, that I have found one who is nearer and dearer to me than you are—that I have found—I know not what.

An angel? No—for every man can say that of his mistress. And yet I am not in a state of mind to tell you circumstantially how perfect she is and why she is so perfect. It is enough to say she has carried captive all my faculties.

So much simplicity with so much understanding—so gentle and yet so animated—such a tranquil spirit with a life of activity and care!

Now all this is miserable declamation—mere abstraction, which does not give you a single trait of her character. Well, then, another time—no, not another time—you must know her *now*—now or never. Yet, to confess a secret to you, I have twice had more than half a mind to throw down my pen, order my horse, and ride over to see her. And yet I made a solemn resolu-

tion not to go there this *morning* and, therefore, run to the
window every moment to see how high the sun is!

I could resist no longer. I could not help going there, and now
that I have come back, my dear William, I will eat my supper
and write to you. What a delight it is to my heart to see her
surrounded with her eight lovely, happy brothers and sisters!

But if I go on at this rate, you will be just as wise at the end
of the letter as you are at the beginning. Listen, then, and I
will compose myself for a detail of facts.

I wrote you sometime since, that I had become acquainted
with M. S————, the Prince's Steward, and that he had invited me to visit him in his hermitage or rather his little empire.
I deferred it and should, perhaps, never have gone if accident
had not discovered to me the treasure which lies concealed there
in silence and obscurity.

The young folks here had arranged a ball in the country,
in which I willingly joined them. I engaged a little girl for
my partner, who was amiable and pretty but not remarkably
interesting, and it was agreed that I should carry her and her
aunt in a coach and call on the way for Charlotte S————.
"You will become acquainted with a very beautiful woman," said
my companion as we passed through a tall and venerable wood to
the hunting lodge. "Take care," added the aunt, "that you do not
lose your heart." "Why so?" said I. "Because," she replied,
"Charlotte is already engaged to a very worthy man who is
now absent to settle some business, to which he must attend in
consequence of the death of his father, and to solicit a very eli-
gible place under the government." The intelligence was quite
indifferent to me.

The sun was just sinking behind the mountains as we reached
the gate of the court yard. The air was very close and the ladies
began to express their fears of a thunder storm, which seemed
to be gathering in dark and lowering clouds round the horizon.
I assumed all my weather wisdom and dissipated *their* fears,
though I myself began to think our amusement might be interrupted.

I got out and a servant girl came to the door and begged
us to wait a moment and Miss Charlotte would be ready. I crossed
the court towards a fine-looking house, and, as I ascended the
steps and entered the door, was struck with the most touching
spectacle I ever beheld. In the anti-chamber before me six chil-

dren from eleven to two years old were dancing round a female figure of fine proportions and the middle size, dressed in a plain white frock, with pink bows on the arms and bosom. She held in her hand a brown loaf and cut from it a slice for each individual in the little circle around her, in proportion to their respective ages and appetites. She distributed it with the most affectionate kindness, and each in return thanked her with the simplest expression of gratitude for the slice for which he had held up his little hands in eager expectation long before it was cut off, and then satisfied with his portion sprang with giddy haste or, according to his more sober disposition, gravely walked to the court-yard gate to see the strangers and the coach that had come to take away their Charlotte. "I must apologize," said she, "for troubling you and the ladies to wait for me, but having been occupied with dressing and making some arrangements for the family during my absence I had forgotten to give my children their supper, and they do not like to receive it from any hands but mine." I made her an awkward compliment. My whole soul was filled with her form and tones and manner, and I had hardly time to recover from my surprise while she was absent in the next room to get her gloves and fan. The smaller children considered me from a cautious distance. I went up to the youngest, who had a very expressive countenance. He retreated until Charlotte entered the door and said: "Shake hands with your cousin, Louis." He did it with open confidence, and I could not refrain from kissing him, dirty as his lips were. "Cousin?" said I, as I gave her my hand to lead her to the carriage. "Do you intend to allow me the privilege of claiming a relationship with you?" "O," said she with a significant smile, "the circle of our cousins is pretty comprehensive and I should be sorry to think you the least worthy of them." As she went away, she told Sophia, who is the eldest of her sisters and about eleven years old, that she must take good care of the children and go to her father as soon as he returned from his ride on horseback. She told the rest that they must mind their sister as they would mind herself, and this they all very freely promised. However, a little self-sufficient, bright-faced girl about six years old added: "She is not Charlotte though, for all that; and we had rather mind you." The two eldest boys had climbed up behind the carriage and at my entreaty she allowed them to ride to the end of the wood, on condition they would take care not to jostle each other and to hold very fast.

We had hardly seated ourselves in the carriage, the ladies had hardly finished their compliments and commonplaces on the roads and the company we were to meet when Charlotte stopped the carriage to let her brothers get down, who again had leave to kiss her hand, which the eldest did with all the gallantry you would expect at fifteen and the youngest with thoughtless vehemence. She sent her love to the little ones and we passed on.

The aunt asked her if she had finished the last book she sent her. "No," said Charlotte, "I did not much like it and will return it, if you please. The first, too, was not more to my taste." I asked her what books they were, and was surprized when she told me they were ———— and ————. Every thing she said was full of character—every instant I found new charms, new expressions of talent beaming from her countenance, while she, on her part, discovered a visible satisfaction in the consciousness that she was understood.

"When I was quite young," she went on, "nothing delighted me so much as romances. Heaven knows how happy I was when I could hide myself in a corner on Sunday and exhaust my feelings over the joys and sorrows of a favourite heroine. I do not mean to deny that this species of writing has still some charms for me, but I have so little time now for reading that I am rather fastidious in my selections. That author has now the most power over me, in whose book, I find a reflection and copy of my own little world—with whom every thing happens, as it happens to myself, and whose story goes to my heart like my own domestick life, which, though it may indeed be no paradise to me, is yet a perpetual source of inexpressible happiness." It cost me a considerable effort to restrain my emotion. However, it did not last long, for when I heard her speak incidentally with so much discrimination of the Vicar of Wakefield, of ———— and ————, I was recollected, went on to pour out all my own knowledge and opinions, and it was not until Charlotte addressed herself to them, that I remembered we had companions with us or remarked that they were looking at me with significant astonishment and that the aunt in particular more than once cast an expressive glance at me, which, however, entirely failed of its intended effect.

The conversation now turned upon the pleasure of dancing. "If this is a sin," said Charlotte, "I must confess I am no saint.

When I am out of spirits, I have only to play a dancing tune upon an ill-tuned harpsichord and it is all over."

With what steadfastness I gazed upon her dark eyes—with what deep emotion I watched her lips and marked the varied expressions of her countenance—how often I was so completely absorbed in the strength and originality of her tho'ts that the language in which they were conveyed escaped me—all this you will easily imagine, for you know me. In short, when we stopped at the dancing-hall I got out of the coach like one in a dream, and was so entirely lost in the world of my own feelings and imagination that I hardly observed the musick which burst upon us from the lighted hall.

The two Adrans and a Mr. Somebody—nobody can remember all sorts of names—who were the aunt's and Charlotte's partners met us at the door and took possession of their ladies and I, at the same time, led off mine.

We began by dancing minuets. I asked one lady after another, and the most awkward and insufferable were precisely those who would not be persuaded to give them up. Charlotte and her partner then began a contra-dance, and I need not tell you what delight I felt, when our turn came to go through the figure with her. You should see her dance—she puts so much of her heart into the act that her whole person seems to be an expression of harmony.* She is as careless and unconstrained as if she were entirely alone—as if she thought of nothing else and felt nothing else—and in truth, for the moment the whole world vanished before her. I asked her to dance the second contra-dance with me. She said she would dance the third, and with the most bewitching frankness told me she was extremely fond of allemandes. "It is the fashion here," said she, "for partners only to dance the allemandes together, but mine dances them very ill and will be obliged to me to excuse him from them. Your partner, too, cannot and will not dance them, and I know from the contra-dance that you must waltz well. Now if you have a mind to go through the allemandes with me, go and ask my partner and I will go and ask your's." I did so, and it was settled that her partner and mine should dance together.

We began, and for some time only amused ourselves with

---

* See *Bride of Abydos*, Note 6. [Ticknor's footnote recalls Zuleika: "The mind, the Music breathing from her face, The heart whose softness harmonized the whole." Byron's note on this passage refers to Mme. de Staël's *De l'Allemagne*. Ed.]

making numberless motions with our arms. With what graceful skill she moved! When we came to the waltz and began to revolve every thing went well at first, because we went slowly, but soon there began to be some confusion. We kept aloof, while they were jostling each other, but when the unskillfull had left the floor, we came in and continued the figure with but one other couple—Adran and his partner. Never was my step so elastick. I was no longer mortal. To hold in my arms the most lovely of women—to glide round the room with her as if borne on air, till every thing about us seemed to grow giddy, and ——— I must, however, confess to you, William, that I then resolved that she whom I should love and who should have promised to be mine should never waltz with another. I need not give you a reason for it.

We walked round the hall to breathe the fresh air. Then she sat down, and the oranges, which I brought her by stealth, because they were the last, refreshed her very much, but every slice she divided with an unmannerly Miss who sat next to her went to my very heart.

In the third contra-dance we were the second couple. As we were going down and as I was gazing—heaven knows with what cordial delight!—on the unmingled pleasure she so frankly expressed in every feature and movement, we came to a lady whom I had before remarked for the benevolence of a countenance which had survived the charm of youth. As we passed her, she smiled at Charlotte, lifted up a threatening finger, and twice repeated, with emphasis, the name of Albert.

"Who is Albert?" said I to Charlotte, "if it be not an impertinent question?" She was about to answer as we were separated to go eight hands round, and I thought I saw a wandering anxiety pass over her brow, as we crossed hands back again. "I know no reason," she replied as she gave me her hand to promenade, "why I should conceal from you that Albert is a very worthy man, to whom I am engaged." Now this was nothing new to me, for my partner had told it to me in the coach, and yet I was entirely unprepared for it, for it had not once occurred to my recollection during the few moments in which she had become so dear to me. I forgot myself, mistook the figure, turned the wrong couple, and confused every thing, and Charlotte was obliged to be every where present, pushing one and pulling another in order to reduce the sett to order.

The dance was not yet finished, when the lightning, which had for some time played in the horizon, and which I had insisted was only heat-lightning, began to be more and more severe, and the musick was drowned in the thunder. Three ladies left the sett, and their partners followed them—the confusion became general and the musick stopped. It is natural that an accident or alarm which happens to us in the midst of our pleasures should touch us more nearly than it would at another time, partly from the contrast, which is then so much more sensibly felt, and partly and principally because, when the feelings are once excited, every thing makes a more lively impression upon them. It is to this cause I ascribe the remarkable terror expressed by most of our ladies. The most courageous placed herself in a corner with her back to the window and stopped her ears. A second knelt before her and hid her face in the other's lap. A third crowded between them and clung to her sister and burst into tears. Some insisted on going home; others, yet more beside themselves, had not self-possession enough left to repress the presumption of their partners, who were stealing from their lips the sighs they addressed to heaven. Some of the gentlemen went off to smoke a quiet pipe, and the rest of the party were not sorry that our landlady had kindness and discretion enough to show us into a chamber that had shutters and curtains. As soon as we reached it, Charlotte went to work and placed the chairs in a circle and, when the party, at her request, were all seated, she proposed a play.

I saw several who lengthened their faces and drew back, in the hope it would be forfeits. "Let us play at counting," said she. "Now take care! I shall go round the circle from right to left, and each of you must count as I come to you. I shall be as quick as thought, and if any body stops or makes a mistake, I shall give him a box on the ear—and so on until we have counted a thousand." It was amusing enough, to be sure, to see her as she moved round the circle with her arms ready extended for the blow. "*One*," said the first—"*Two*," the second—"*Three*," the next, and so on. Then she began to go faster and faster. One made a mistake and received his punishment—the next, from his laughter, succeeded no better—and still she continued going faster and faster. I had two blows for my share and flattered myself with the belief that they were harder than those she gave to the rest. An universal laughter and confusion ended the game long before we had reached our thousand. The party, who had now recovered their composure, separated—the storm was over and I followed Charlotte into the hall. As we passed along, she said, "The blows have made them forget the storm and every thing else." I could make her no answer. "I was," she added, "one of the most timid of the company, but in the attempt to give courage to the rest I found it for myself." We went to a window. The thunder rolled at a distance—a gentle rain distilled on the fields—and the air was filled with the most refreshing fragrance. She leaned upon her arm, and her eye wandered over the landscape—then was raised to heaven—and then fell on me. I saw that it was full of tears. She laid her hand on mine and said—"Klopstock!"—I remembered the exquisite lines that were then present to her thoughts and was overwhelmed with the crowd of feelings and associations which that single word poured upon me. I could not prevent it—I bent over her hand and kissed it with tears of delight. I looked again in her eyes— Divine Poet! would to Heaven thou couldst have seen thine apotheosis in that glance—and that this might be the *last* time I shall ever hear that name repeated, which has been so often profaned!

June 19

Where I left my story is more than I can tell—all I know is that it was II o'clk when I went to bed, and that if I could have talked instead of written to you, I should probably have kept you up till morning.

I believe I did not tell you what happened to us on our return from the ball, and now I have no time for it.

The sun rose with uncommon splendour on the glittering woods and refreshed landscape. Our companions fell asleep. She asked me if I did not wish to join the party and begged me not to keep awake on her account. "As long as you are awake," said I looking steadfastly at her, "there is no danger." We were both still awake when we reached her door, which the maid opened very softly and, in reply to Charlotte's inquiry, told her that her father and the children were well and still asleep. There I left her, after asking and obtaining leave to visit her again in the course of the day. I went—and since that time sun, moon, and stars have fulfill'd their courses unnoticed—I know not when it is day or night—the whole world fades and disappears before me.

June 21

My days are as happy as those which Heaven has prepared for the elect, and whatever may hereafter befall me, I shall never dare to say that I have not tasted the purest pleasure which this world can afford.* You know my Walheim—well, I am established there, and there I am but half a league from Charlotte—there I am myself again—and there I enjoy as much happiness as can be enjoyed by man.

Little did I imagine, when I made Walheim the limit of my walks, that it was so near the confines of Heaven! How often, in the course of my wanderings, have I looked with idle curiosity, sometimes from the hill and sometimes from the meadow on the opposite side of the river, towards that hunting-lodge, which is now the home and centre of all my hopes!

I have often, my dear William, reflected on the disposition of every man to wander far and wide in search of new discoveries, and, after all, at the voice of nature from within him to retreat gladly within his old boundaries and regular habits and cease to seek for happiness any where but at home.

It is very remarkable: When I first came here and looked from this hill, every thing was gay with promise. Perhaps I turned towards the little wood, and there I thought I should find refreshing shades. Perhaps I gazed at the summit of the mountain, and there I was sure a various landscape would be spread out before me. Perhaps I looked towards the hills which intersected each other in all directions and formed such luxuriant vallies; and in that labyrinth I thought I could lose myself with delight! I rushed forward to seize the promised pleasures and returned without having found a resting-place for my hopes.

Is it not with distance as it is with futurity? A dark and doubtful cloud settles on the prospect—our imagination like our vision trembles before it—and we long to cast away our very existence to be able to gratify to satiety this single unsatisfied and insatiable passion. And at last, when we have attained the object—when the future has become present—all is still the same —we are still consumed by the same craving curiosity and still

---

* "And come what may I *have been* blest." *Giaour*. [Ticknor's reference to Byron's poem is followed by a pencilled quotation from Schiller's *Picolomini* (III, 7): "Ich habe gelebt und geliebet." These words appear with no indication of source or date, but they indicate the definite possibility that Ticknor took his MS to Europe. Ed.]

constrained by the same barriers—and the heart now languishes for pleasures which can never return.

The most restless of spirits comes back, at last, to the land of his fathers—and finds in his cottage, in the bosom of his wife, in the circle of his children, in his very struggles for their support, a pleasure which he had sought in vain through the wide world.

When I rise in the morning with the sun and go into my garden, gather my pease, sit down there, and, at alternate intervals, shell them and read in my Homer—when I take out the kettle in the little kitchen, put the butter in it, hang the pease over the fire, cover them up, and sit down and stir them—then I am as gay as the presumptuous suitors of Penelope, who killed and cut up and roasted her hogs and oxen.

Nothing fills me with such tranquil delight as the descriptions we have of patriarchal life—a life, which, I gratefully acknowledge, I can make my own without affectation. It is impossible for me to tell you how happy I am that I have a heart which can enjoy the simple and innocent pleasure of the peasant, who brings to his table a cabbage he has himself cultivated and who enjoys in a single moment not merely the vegetable itself, but all the happy days he spent in cherishing it—the fair morning in which he planted it—and the mild evenings in which he watered it and was gladdened by its gradual growth.

June 29

Day before yesterday the physician of the place called at the Steward's and found me on the floor among Charlotte's children, some of whom were climbing over me and others pulling me about, while I was employed in tickling them, so that, on the whole, we made a great noise. The doctor, who is a very dogmatical piece of formality—and was occupied during the conversation in composing his ruffles into their folds and perpetually pulling up his cravath, tho't this conduct quite beneath the dignity of a man, at least his countenance told me so. However, I did not suffer him to restrain me but continued to allow the children to treat me with very little ceremony, and built up their cardhouses as often as they pulled them down. When he returned to town, he said: The Steward's children were rude enough before, but Werter had fairly spoiled them.

Yes, my dear William, nothing on earth touches my heart so nearly as children. When I look at them and see in their little

spirits the seeds of all those virtues and talents which will hereafter be so necessary to them, when I see in the obstinate the
indications of future independence and firmness; in the giddy,
that good-nature and cheerfulness which will lead them lightly
over the sorrows of life—when I see them so unpractised, so pure
—then, *then* I remember the words of him who spake as never
man spake: "Unless ye become as one of these little children . . ."!
And yet these, who are certainly our equals, and whom we ought
to regard as our models—we treat them as if they were our
slaves. We do not suffer them even to have a will! Have *we*, then,
none? And where is the difference? Is it only, that we are older
and more practised? God of mercy! who beholdest from the throne
great children and little children, but nought else, thou hast de-
clared by the Son in which of them thou hast most delight. But
the world believe him and obey him not, as it was of old, and teach
their children to follow in their steps, and—Farewell, my dear
William, I must not indulge myself in this way.

July 1

What Charlotte can do for the sick, I know from experience,
for my own wretched heart has been more diseased than many
a man who languishes on a bed of sickness. She has now gone to
pass a few days with an excellent friend in town, who, in the
opinion of her physicians, is drawing near to the grave and wishes
to have Charlotte with her in her last moments.

I went with her last week to visit the Curate of St. ———,
a small village about a league from here out towards the
mountains. We arrived there at about IV o'clock. Charlotte carried her youngest sister with her. As we entered the yard before
the parsonage, which was shaded by two tall walnut-trees, the
good old man was sitting before his door upon a bench, but
the moment he saw Charlotte he seemed inspired with new life,
forgot his crutch, and came forward to meet her. She ran to
him, compelled him to resume his seat, and sat down by him—
gave him her father's respects and played with a little scrubby,
dirty boy, the idol of his old age. You should have seen her—you
should have seen how deep an interest she took in the old man
—how she raised her voice to meet his deafness—what accounts
she gave him of those who had died in the flower and strength
of youth—how she praised the virtues of the Carlstadt waters,
encouraged his determination to go there the next summer, and

told him he looked much better and brighter than he did the last time she saw him.—In the mean time, I had paid my respects to the old lady.—The curate's spirits rose, and, as I could not refrain from praising the fine walnut-trees, which cast so refreshing a shade upon us, he immediately began, though with some difficulty, to give us their history. "As for the eldest," said he, "we don't know who planted it—some say one curate and some, another. The youngest, however, which stands just beyond it, is exactly the age of my wife—fifty years old next October. Her father planted it in the morning, and she was born in the evening. He was my predecessor, and I cannot tell you how much he cherished that tree—and it is no less dear to me. My wife sat on a log under it knitting the first time I ever entered this yard and when I was a poor student." Charlotte asked after his daughter. He said she was gone with Mr. Smith to the workmen in the field—and then resumed his story and told us how he won the favour of the curate and of his daughter and became first his vicar and then his successor. The history was hardly finished, when the daughter and Mr. Smith crossed the garden towards us. She received Charlotte with cordial kindness, and, I must needs says, her looks pleased me very well. She is a lively well-formed brunette, with whom a man might pass his life very pleasantly in the country. Her lover (for such I immediately discovered Mr. Smith to be) was a reserved, silent man, who did not join at all in our conversation, though Charlotte endeavoured to draw him out. What concerned me the most was to see in his physiognomy that he was hindered by ill-humour rather than by want of understanding. Immediately afterwards this suspicion was but too well justified, for, as Frances was walking with Charlotte and of course occasionally with me, this gentleman's countenance, which is at best rather sallow, became suddenly so dark and threatening, that Charlotte pulled me by the sleeve to let me know I was rather too attentive to Frances. Now nothing grieves me more than that people torment one another in this way, and especially that the young, in the bloom of life, when their hearts are most alive to pleasure, should thus embitter the few bright moments that are allowed them, and find out their mistake only when it is too late to correct it. It went to my very heart—and when we returned to the parsonage at nightfall and sat down to a supper of milk and the conversation turned on the joys and sorrows of life, I could not resist the temptation which the subject offered me to utter a phillippick against ill-humor. "We very often complain," I began, "that we have so little happiness and so much misery, but, in my opinion, the complaint is altogether unreasonable. If we had affectionate hearts to enjoy the good which God's daily bounty offers to us, we should easily acquire fortitude enough to bear the evils that may befal us." "But we have not our disposition completely in our power," said the curate's wife. "A great deal depends on the body, and when that is diseased every thing goes wrong." "I agree with you entirely," said I. "Let us then consider it a disease and see if we cannot find a specifick for it." "That is something to the purpose," said Charlotte. "I have no doubt a great deal depends on ourselves, for I have found it so in my own case. When any thing troubles me and oppresses my spirits, I leave my work and take a turn in the garden and sing a lively air, and it is all over." "That is exactly what I mean," said I, "ill-humour is like sloth, and, in fact, is a species of sloth. We are, by nature, indolent and yet, when we have once found resolution enough to become industrious, labour ceases to be irksome, and we find a real pleasure in activity." Frances was very attentive. The young man objected that "we cannot have such an absolute empire over ourselves and least of all over our feelings." "But the question now," I replied, "is concerning a perverse disposition, which is a misery to everybody, and no man can tell how much power he has over himself, until he has tried the experiment. When a man is sick, he calls in many physicians and takes with exemplary patience the most nauseous medicine in order to recover his health." I observed that the good old man laboured to hear me, and therefore, addressing myself to him and raising my voice, I added, "We have sermons against almost every form of sin, but I have never heard that any body has preached against the sin of ill-humour."* *That*, he said, was a subject for metropolitans, for in the country they had no such thing as ill-humour, though, he thought, it might be well enough to preach a discourse on it now and then, if it were only for the benefit of the Steward and of his wife. We all laughed and he, too, laughed very heartily, until he brought on a coughing fit, which interrupted the conversation for some time. The young man then resumed the subject. "You call ill-humour 'a crime', " said he. "This seems to me to be too severe."

---

* There is, however, an exquisite sermon against it by Lavater—to say nothing of the Book of Jonah.

"Not at all," I replied, "if that deserves the name which injures both ourselves and our neighbour. Is it not enough that we cannot add to each other's happiness but must we, also, labour to deprive each other of those pleasures which each might enjoy by himself? And show me the man who has a perverse disposition and has generosity enough to conceal it, to bear it alone, and to refrain from poisoning the pleasures of those about him. Besides, does it not proceed from a secret soreness on account of our own un- worthiness—from a distrust of ourselves, which is always united with an envy that is the very offspring of a weak vanity. We can- not, forsooth, endure to see men happy whom *we* have not made so." Charlotte smiled at the earnestness with which I spoke, but a tear in Frances's eye still urged me forward. "Woe to him," said I, "woe to him, who uses the power he has over another's heart to deprive it of those simple pleasures which are its natural inheritance. All the wealth, all the kindness in the world will never compensate for the loss of a moment of that pure pleasure, which the envy and perverseness of our tyranny has poisoned in its source."

My heart was full almost to bursting—the recollection of many a past scene rushed on my mind and filled my eyes with tears.

"Why should we not say to ourselves every day: We can do nothing for those we love but to leave them in quiet possession of their peculiar pleasures and add to these others which they can- not procure for themselves and which we can share with them. For when they are tormented with passion or bent under the bur- then of sorrow and suffering, how can we hope to give them even a transitory consolation?"

"And when the last desperate disease has seized the victim, whom you have hurried to an untimely grave, when she lies be- fore you languishing and exhausted—when her darkened eye is fixed on heaven and the dampness of death has gathered on her pale forehead—*then* you will stand before her like a condemned malefactor, in the full persuasion that all you can now do will no longer avail—*then* you will need no punishment more terrible than the conviction, which will press on your heart, that the sacri- fice of all you have and all you hope would not invigorate her with a moment's strength or shed on her departing spirit a single ray of consolation."

The recollection of a scene like this, at which I was once

present, rose distinctly before me. I hid my face in my handkerchief and left the room, and nothing but Charlotte's voice summoning me to return with her recalled me to myself. On our way she tenderly reproached me for the deep interest I take in every thing—told me it would impair my health—and that I must take care of myself. Angel of light! for thy dear sake, I *will* live!

July 6

She is still with her dying friend—still the same benevolent spirit that alleviates sorrow and carries happiness wherever she goes. She went to walk last evening with Mary-Ann and little Martha. As I knew her intention, I went to meet them and we took our walk together. On the road about a league and an half towards the town we came to the fountain, which was always so dear to me and is now a thousand times dearer than ever. Charlotte sat down on the top of the bank and we stood up before her. I looked around me, and the days in which my heart was so lonely rose to my imagination. "Sweet fountain," said I, "since that time I have no longer sought your refreshing coolness, and in my impatience and haste have often passed on without even noticing you!" I looked down and saw little Martha coming very cautiously towards us with a glass of water.—I turned towards Charlotte, and felt all I possess in her.—At this moment Martha came up with her glass, and Mary-Ann wanted to take it. "No," said the child in the most touching tone, "*you* must drink first, Charlotte." I was so much delighted with this simple expression of affection, that, in the ardour of my feelings, I caught up the child and kissed her so rudely that she began to cry. "You have done wrong," said Charlotte. I was sorry for it. "Come Martha," said she, as she took her by the hand and led her down the steps, "there—go and wash yourself at the spring and the water will take it all out." I stood still, and saw how sedulously she rubbed her cheeks, and with what unwavering faith she believed the virtues of the fountain would wash away her shame and efface the impression that had been left by my rudeness and my beard. At last Charlotte told her it was enough, but still the child continued her lustration, as if she were more afraid of doing too little than too much. I assure you, William, I never looked with more reverence on a baptism—and when Charlotte came up I could willingly have fallen down and worshipped her, as I would have worshipped a prophet who had just returned from washing away the sins of an empire.

In the evening I could not help telling the story in the fulness of my heart to a man who, because he had talents, I used to suppose had common sense, but I was miserably mistaken. He said Charlotte was wrong, that we should never deceive children in any way, and above all should beware of filling their heads with nonsense and superstition. I recollected that he had been dipped a week before and did not press the matter, though I remained firm to my original belief: That we should treat children as God treats us, who suffers us to find some of our truest pleasures in harmless delusions.

July 8

What a child I am! What an unreasonable value I place on a single look! What a child I am! We had been to Walheim. The ladies got out to walk and, as we went, I thought I saw in Charlotte's dark eyes—I am a fool! Forgive me for it! But if you could have seen those eyes—However, to be brief (for it is very late) when the ladies got in again, young W———, Seltstadt, Adran, and myself stood by the carriage. There was a good deal of talking and laughing with the young men from the coach-window and, to say the truth, they were very gay and pleasant. I endeavoured to catch Charlotte's eye. It wandered from one to another, but upon me—*me* who stood there with no thought but of her—it did not rest on *me!* My heart bade her farewell a thousand times, and yet she did not notice me! The carriage drove off, and the tears sprang into my eyes. I looked after it and saw her lean her head out of the window and look back—but was it to see *me?* My dear William, I rest on this uncertainty—*this* is my comforter: *Perhaps* she looked back to see *me! Perhaps!* Good night—I am but a child!—

July 10

You cannot imagine how foolishly I look when her name is mentioned in conversation or when I am asked how I *like* her? *Like!* I hate that word worse than the grave! What kind of a man must he be who *likes* Charlotte—all whose faculties and feelings are not filled by her? How I *like* her? Why, a man asked me the other day how I *liked Ossian?*

July 11

Mrs. M——— is very sick. I pray for her life, because I am interested in all Charlotte's sorrows. I see her occasionally at a friend's house, and to-day she told me a singular story. Mr. M——— is a cold, proud miser, who has troubled and restrained his wife all he could, though in return he has received from her nothing but kindness and attention. A few days ago, when the physicians had given her over, she sent for her husband and in Charlotte's presence told him that she had something to explain to him which might otherwise raise doubts and difficulty after her death. "I have always," said she, "managed your domestick affairs with as much regularity and economy as possible, and you must forgive me that in one thing I have deceived you for thirty years. At the time of our marriage you allowed me something for the expences of the table and other domestick wants. As our establishment and income increased, you did not in the same proportion enlarge my weekly allowance—in short, you supposed that at the time our affairs were the most prosperous I ought still to go on with seven florins a week. I consented to it without murmuring and was able to save a weekly surplus from my expences greater than any body might have thought a woman would choose to lock up. Of this I have spent nothing and should not now have mentioned it, if it were not that my house-keeper will be left in unprotected poverty without it, and that you may always be able to say with confidence, that your first wife was satisfied."

I talked with Charlotte on the remarkable union of different talents that was necessary to enable a woman to effect that with seven florins which is not commonly done with less than twice the amount. I have, however, met with a few people myself who seemed to have received the prophet's inexhaustible oil-cruise without a miracle.

July 13

No, I do not deceive myself! I read in her dark eyes the deep interest she takes in me and in my destiny. Yes, I feel it, and dare to trust my heart with the assurance that she—O! may I, can I express all heaven in one word—that she loves me!

Yes, she loves me, and I dare to tell *you*, William—for *you*

have a soul that will comprehend my meaning—I dare to tell you how I respect, how I honour myself, *because* she loves me!

Is it from presumption or from the sober certainty of waking bliss that I dare to say I know not the man who can make me tremble for my place in Charlotte's heart. And yet, when she speaks of Albert and speaks of him, too, with so much kindness, so much affection, I feel like one who is instantly stripped of his honours, his rank, and his sword.

July 16

How my blood quickens in its course if only her finger touches me—if our feet happen to meet under the table! I shrink, as if from a flame, but immediately a secret impulse urges me forward again, until every thing grows giddy around me. Her pure and unpractised heart does not suspect the torments I feel when she shows me any little familiarity—when in the earnestness of conversation she lays her hand on mine or leans forward towards me, until her breath is borne to my very lips and I feel ready to sink to the earth, as if I had been struck by a thunderbolt. —And yet if I should ever presume upon this openness—! No, William, my heart is not corrupt—weak, *very* weak, I admit—and is not that guilt?

She is hallowed in my sight! All presumption is repressed in her presence. I know not why it is, but when I am with her every fibre seems to be quick with intelligence.

There is a simple, touching air which she plays on her harpsichord, with the expression of an angel. It is her favourite—and the moment she touches the first note, my pains and cares and sorrows vanish. I no longer doubt the miracles of ancient musick, since I have felt the power of this simple air. When I am ready to lay down my life, as a weary load, she plays this tune, and the doubt and darkness of my soul are instantly dissipated and I am again restored to light and life.

July 18

What, my dear William, is all the world to our heart, without love? It is a magick lanthorn without its light. Bring but its lamp into it, and the wall is instantly covered with pictures of gaiety and life. And even if it be nothing else—nothing but a transitory shadow, still it is the source of our happiness so long as we can look on, like thoughtless children and find delight in the unsubstantial vision.

I was detained from visiting Charlotte to-day by some tire-some company. What should I do? Why, I sent my servant to her, merely for the sake of having somebody with me who had to-day been within the sphere of her influence. How impatiently I waited for his return, and with what transport I gazed on him when he came! I should have taken him in my arms and kissed him, if I had not been ashamed to do it!

We are told of the Bologna stone, which by lying in the sun absorbs its rays and becomes itself luminous during a part of the subsequent night. Just so it was with my servant: The spirit and sensibility which had beamed from her eyes upon his countenance, upon the buttons of his coat and the lace on his cape, had dignified and consecrated him in my sight. At that moment, I would not have taken a thousand crowns for him—his presence filled me with such delight.

Heaven forbid that you should make yourself merry with this!—Can that be unreal which constitutes our happiness?

July 19

"I shall see her to-day"—I exclaim in the morning when I awake and look with a light heart at the rising sun—"I shall see her to-day"—and for the whole day I know no other wish. Every thing else fades before this prospect—*every thing*!

July 20

I cannot agree with you that it is best for me to go to the ambassador at ———. I am not very fond of subordination, and we all know that he is a man of form and ceremony. My mother, you say, wishes me to be in more active life. Am I, then, idle now? Can there be such a mighty difference between such miserable trifles? The world, indeed, is in the perpetual pursuit of vanity, but he who to please another and in opposition to his own feelings and dispositions labours in any profession what-ever to gain wealth or honour is a madman.

July 24

Since you are so anxious that I should not neglect my draw-ing, I would much rather avoid the subject altogether than tell you that I have done very little. Yet I never was happier—my perception of natural beauty, even in its minutest details, was never more full and intimate and still—I know not why it is so, but when I come to the trial all my accustomed skill vanishes, every thing swims and trembles before me, and I labour in vain to catch even an outline. However, I think if I had clay or wax I should do better. I shall, therefore, take clay, if this indisposition continues, and go to kneading and baking.

Three times I have attempted Charlotte's picture and three times I have dishonoured my pencil. And this is the more mortifying to me as I was once very happy in catching a likeness. To supply its place I have taken her profile and must be content with *that*.

July 26

Yes, my dear Charlotte, I will be very careful to do your errand—only give me such commissions often, *very* often. Let me, however, ask one thing of you: not to sand the notes you write me, for to-day, when I pressed it to my lips, it sat my teeth on edge.

July 26

I have very often resolved that I would visit her less frequently. But who could keep such a resolution? Every day I yield to the temptation and every day I promise myself anew— "To-morrow you will, for once, stay away."—But when to-morrow comes I still find some irresistible reason for going, and before I think of it again I am with her. Either she had said to me the evening before, "We shall see you to-morrow"—and then who could stay away?—Or she had given me some errand, and I imagine that nobody but myself can carry the answer—Or the fine weather leads me to Walheim, and when I am there I am but half a league from Charlotte—I am, in fact, within the very influence of her atmosphere, and before I have determined to go on, *there* I am again.

My grandmother used to tell me a story of a loadstone mountain. The ships which came too near it were in an instant deprived of their iron-works, the nails flew to the mountain, and the miserable wretches on board perished, amidst the disjointed planks.

July 30

Albert has come and I must go. If he were the best man in the world, one whom I should be willing to acknowledge as my superior in every respect, it would still be intolerable to me to see him in my very presence in possession of so much perfection.—Possession?—Yes, William, for is he not her acknowledged lover? A generous, amiable man I know, but still her lover. Fortunately I was not there when he first came. It would have broken my heart. He has had the generosity, too, to restrain his expressions of fondness for Charlotte, whenever I have been present. God reward him for it! I should love him, if it were only because he loves Charlotte. He likes me, but I suspect his regard is rather reflected from Charlotte than original in himself. Women are very dexterous in such matters and are right to be so, for if they can keep up a good understanding between two lovers it is always for their advantage, seldom as it happens.

I cannot, after all, refuse my regard to Albert. The even tranquillity of his deportment forms a striking contrast to my ungovernable impetuosity. Still he has a great deal of feeling and knows what he possesses in Charlotte. He seems to have very little ill-humour, which you know is, in my estimation, the deadliest of the deadly sins.

He considers me a man of talents, and my dependence on Charlotte and the open interest I take in whatever relates to her only increase his triumph and attachment. Whether he does not sometimes trouble her with a little jealousy is more than I know, but this I know, that if I were in his place I should not be entirely free from the foul fiend.

Let that be as it may, the days of my happiness with Charlotte are over.—Shall I call it folly or blindness?—But what need is there of a name, when the fact tells its own tale? I knew every thing I now know before Albert returned—I knew I could have no pretensions to her and I made none—I mean, as far as it was possible to make none—and yet now, *now* that another has actually come to take her from me, I am lost in astonishment and dismay.

I should go mad—I should look with thrice told scorn upon the man who could advise me to be calm, because things cannot be otherwise than they are—Spare me, spare me from the curse of such comforters!—I ran through the wood and when I reached Charlotte she was sitting with Albert in the arbour in the garden. I could endure it no longer and spent my feelings in playing the fool and uttering a thousand extravagances. "For Heaven's sake," said Charlotte to me to-day, "let us have no more such

exhibitions as we had last evening. Your high spirits are absolutely alarming."

Between ourselves, I watch my opportunity and go there
when I am sure he is busy, and if I find her alone I am happy.

Aug. 8

I beg you would not think I intended *you*, my dear William,
when I prayed to be delivered from those men who exact uniform
submission under inevitable evil. I assure you, I did not then
think you *could* entertain such an opinion. I admit you are right
in every thing but one: You must not think you can always
restrain a man to the two sides of an alternative for there is as
much difference in feeling and action in the world as there is in
feature and complexion.

You will not, therefore, be offended if I first admit the whole
of your argument and then endeavour to escape between the two
horns of your dilemma.

"Either," you tell me, "you have some hopes of Charlotte, *or*
you have not. Well, in the first case, continue the pursuit and
seek to accomplish your wishes. In the second, summon your
resolution and dismiss a passion, which, at last, will but palsy
all your faculties." My dear William, this is very *well* said and—
very *easily* said, too.

And can you then ask the wretch who is sinking under the
gradual progress of a secret disease—can you bid *him* summon
his resolution and end his sufferings? Does not the very malady
which wastes his strength at the same time take from him his
resolution?

True, you can answer me with another comparison: Who
would not rather lose an arm than wait until his weakness and
irresolution have endangered his life? I know not that any
body would—and we will not quarrel about comparisons. Indeed,
indeed, William, I often feel for a single moment the spirit of
resolution and activity grow strong within me, and at these times
I *could* go, if I but knew where I should find a resting-place.

Evening

My Journal, which I have for a long time neglected, fell into
my hands by accident to-day, and I am surprised to find how
coolly and accurately I have marked every step of my progress—
how justly I have always considered the circumstances in which

I have been placed and yet how weakly I have acted—how clearly
I have seen and yet how blindly I have walked.

Aug. 10

If I were not beside myself, I should be perfectly happy, for
it is very seldom that so many circumstances concur to satisfy
the desires of man as concur in my own case. So true it is, that
the heart must make its own happiness.

To be a part of the most amiable family in the world—to be
loved by the father like a son and by the children like a father,
and by Charlotte, too—! Then there is the generous Albert,
who never attempts with fretful perversity to disturb my enjoyment, who is drawn to me by the truest friendship, and who loves
me above every thing else in the world except Charlotte. It
would delight you, my dear William, to hear our conversations
about Charlotte as we take our walks together. It is indeed, the
strangest connexion in the world, and yet the thought of it often
fills my eyes with tears.

When he speaks to me of her admirable mother and tells me
how, on her death bed, she surrendered her family and children
to Charlotte and solemnly charged her to be faithful to them—
how instantly Charlotte assumed a new character—with what
care she superintended the domestick economy and became in
deed and in truth a mother to the children—with what ceaseless
activity she has since then filled up every moment of her time
and yet has lost none of the happy vivacity of her disposition—I
walk closer to him, pluck the flowers on the way-side, arrange
them with care into a bouquet, and then—throw them into the
passing stream and watch them as they glide slowly away.

I know not whether I have told you that Albert will remain
here and receive a comfortable office under the government, with
whom he is a great favourite. I have very seldom seen any one
so regular and diligent in business.

Aug. 12

Albert is, indeed, the best man in the world. I had a very
remarkable conversation with him yesterday. I went to take
leave of him—for I had a mind to make an excursion to the
mountains (whence I now write you)—and as we were walking
up and down the room, I happened to cast my eyes on his pistols.
"Will you lend me your pistols for my journey?" said I. "With

all my heart," he replied, "if you will take the trouble to load them, for they hang here only for form's sake." I took down one of them. "My caution was once the cause of a distressing accident," he added, "and since then I have had nothing to do with fire arms." I was curious to learn the particulars. "I was spending three months with a friend in the country," said he, "and had a pair of pocket pistols with me unloaded and yet slept in peace. At last, as I was sitting in idleness on a rainy forenoon, I know not how it came into my head, but I began to imagine we might be attacked, might want the pocket-pistols and might—you know how we go on from one thing to another. So I gave them to the servant to clean and load and he must needs amuse himself with frightening the maid and—heaven knows how it happened!—but the pistol went off with the ramrod in it and the ramrod struck the maid here, in the fleshy part of her hand, and tore off her thumb. Then we had lamentations enough and the surgeon's bill besides, and so, since that time, I have kept no loaded pistols. After all, my dear fellow, what is foresight? Danger will not send us warning. To say truth, however—" Now, do you know, I like every thing about this man but his 'to say truths'—a remark which you must not take to yourself since every rule has its exceptions. But Albert is so precisely rational that when he has made an assertion which savours of precipitation or extravagance there is no end of his limitations and modifications and recantations, till at last it is reduced to just nothing at all. On the present occasion, he entered into a long explanation of his remark. I soon ceased to listen, fell into a reverie and by an accidental movement raised the muzzle of the pistol to my forehead, just above my right eye. "Take care!" said Albert snatching the pistol from me. "What do you mean by that?" "It is not loaded," said I. "Well, what of that?" he replied impatiently. "I cannot believe a man should be so mad as to shoot himself. The mere thought of it shocks me."

"Why is it necessary," I cried, "to determine so quickly that any action is weak or wise or honourable or disgraceful? What name will you give to such precipitation? Have you considered the deep motives which determine conduct? Have you learnt how to disentangle and explain the reasons why it happened, and why it could not be avoided? If you had, you would not have been so hasty in your judgement."

"Still," said Albert, "you will grant me that some conduct is wicked in itself, whatever may be its motives?"

I shrugged up my shoulders and assented. "Nevertheless, my dear Sir," I went on, "there are some exceptions even to this rule. Stealing is a crime, but is not the man who, to save himself and his family from present famine and death, becomes a robber— is not he the object of pity rather than punishment? Who shall cast the first stone at the husband who sacrifices to his just indignation a faithless wife and her infamous seducer?—or at the girl who is ruined in an unguarded hour by her affection and confidence? Our very laws, cold and formal as they are, melt to mercy in such cases."

"That is quite another affair," said Albert. "A man who is subdued by his passions loses all power of reflection and is to be considered as a drunkard or a madman."

"Yes," said I smiling, "you who are the children of tranquillity, *you* can talk of passion and excess and insanity—*you* can stand in untempted discretion and revile the intemperate and shrink from the maniack—*you* pass by on the other side with the Priest, and with the Pharisee thank God that you are not as one of these! I have more than once drunken to excess—my passions were never far from insanity, and I am ashamed of neither, for I find that all uncommon spirits—all who dare to attempt any thing great or apparently impracticable, must always be reproached as intoxicated madmen. In common life, too, the moment a man does any thing singularly generous and noble, all the world cry out, 'he is beside himself, he is out of his senses!' Take shame to yourselves, ye men of cool temperaments!—Take shame to yourselves, ye men of discretion!"

"This now is just one of your extravagancies," said Albert. "You always go too far and here you are certainly wrong, for you confound suicide, of which we are talking, with heroism, whereas it is impossible to consider it any thing but a weakness, because it is clearly easier to die than to bear with resolution a life of suffering."

I was on the point of breaking up the conversation, for nothing throws me off my balance so surely as to have a man come in upon me unexpectedly with a common-place objection, when I am speaking from the very depths of my heart. However, I restrained myself (for I have been very often met and vexed by it) and answered him with some earnestness: "You call it weakness! Be not deceived by appearances! Will you dare to call that people *weak*, who, after suffering long under the yoke of a tyrant, at last recover their strength and burst their chains? Will you call that man *weak*, who, when a conflagration has reached his house, finds his powers increased by his fears and easily carries burthens which, in a soberer moment, he could hardly have moved? Will you call him *weak*, who, with a courage gathered from despair, resists and defeats alone a band of assassins? No, my good friend, if resistance be a proof of strength, how can the highest degree of resistance be weakness?" Albert stared at me and said, "Pardon me if I confess that the examples you have alledged seem to have nothing to do with the question."

"It is very probable," said I. "I have been very often told that my comparisons have a leaven of absurdity in them. Let us, then, see if we cannot in some other way discover courage in a man who resolves to cast away that burthen which all the rest of the world delight to bear—for we have a right to judge him no farther than we can enter into his peculiar feelings and sympathies."—

"Human nature," I went on, "has its limits. It can endure joy, sorrow, or suffering only to a certain point, and sinks as soon as *that* is past. The question, therefore, is not whether a man be weak or strong, but whether he can endure the weight of his suffering, let that suffering be moral or physical. I think, therefore, it would be as unreasonable to say that a man is a coward who takes away his own life as it would be unprecedented to call *him* a coward, who dies of a malignant fever."

"Paradox, mere paradox," said Albert. "Not so paradoxical as you imagine," I replied. "We call that a mortal disease by which nature is so subdued and its powers so wasted and deranged that they cannot gather strength enough to restore the machinery to its accustomed action. Now, my good friend, let us apply this to the mind. Look into the recesses of a man's soul, mark how deeply impressions are stamped there, how his thoughts beset him round, how a passion, which has increased unnoticed and unknown, destroys his peace forever, and he sinks under its oppression. It is in vain that a man of a cool and rational temper looks down upon the situation of this unfortunate

being—it is in vain that he councils him with the words of
prudence, for he is like a man in health, who can watch, indeed,
at the sick-man's bed, but cannot impart to him the smallest
portion of his own strength."

Albert said the argument was too general. I recollected the
particular case of a girl who had drowned herself a little while
ago and repeated her story to him. "She was a child of simplicity who had grown up contented in the narrow circle of domestick duties and weekly labours—who knew no pleasure except
a Sunday-walk with her companions, dressed in her finest clothes,
and perhaps a single dance at the holidays—and the rest of her
time was satisfied to discourse for hours together with a neighbour on the causes of some petty quarrel or some scandalous report. In time, however, she begins to feel an aching void in her
heart, her former enjoyments become by degrees insipid, and at
last she accidentally meets one to whom she is irresistibly attached by a secret instinct and to whom all her hopes are now
directed. The world fades before her—she hears nothing, sees
nothing, feels nothing, asks nothing but him and him alone. She
is not impelled by an idle and unsettled vanity. Her desires are
bent directly and constantly on their object. She hopes to find in
an indissoluble union with him all the support she needs—all the
fulness of happiness her heart can desire. His repeated promises, which seem to seal the assurance of all her hopes, his en-
dearing fondness, which only increases her passion, occupy every
thought and feeling of her heart. She is absorbed in the consciousness of present happiness and in the anticipation of joys
yet to come—she has reached the very summit of her hopes,
stretches out her arms to meet their fulfillment and finds herself—abandoned. Amazed, frantick, she stands on the brink of
the precipice—all is darkness around her—no hope, no consolation, no *dawn* of hope—for she is forsaken by *him*, with whose
existence her own was identified. She cannot see the world that
is passing before her—she cannot see the many who would pour
balm into her wounded spirit—she feels that she is alone, that
she is abandoned—and, driven forward by the anguish of her
thoughts, casts herself from the precipice and finds in the narrow
house a release from all her sufferings.—This, Albert, *this* is
more than the history of an individual—and is it not, also, the
very workings of disease? Nature strives in vain to escape from

the labyrinth of the confounded and conflicting faculties and at last sinks under the effort. Woe to that man who can look on and say: A foolish girl! if she had but waited—if she had but afforded an opportunity for the operation of time, she would have found another to console her sorrows. This is exactly as if you should say: A foolish fellow to die of a fever!—if he had but waited till he had recovered his strength, till he had purified his circulations and quieted the tumult of his blood, every thing would have gone well and he might have been alive to this day!"

Albert, who saw no resemblance in this comparison, still objected, and among other things said I had taken the case of an ignorant girl, and that it was still impossible for him to conceive that a man of understanding, whose ideas would not be so confined, and who would see things in a wider relation, could possibly destroy himself. "My dear friend," I replied, "a man is *but* a man after all, and the feeble light of reason which the wisest may have will avail very little for his direction, when he is torn with passion and feels the limits of his nature press hard upon him. Besides—but we will settle this question another time," said I and took my hat. My heart was full—and we separated without having understood each other. O, how hard it is for people to understand each other in this world.

Aug. 15

It is certainly true that nothing is absolutely necessary to us in this world but love.—I am sure that Charlotte would part from me with regret, and the children have no other desire than that I should return to them every morning.—To day I went there to tune Charlotte's piano forte. The children begged me to tell them a story, and Charlotte, too, said I had better gratify them. So I cut their evening's supper for them, which they now receive as willingly from me as from Charlotte and told them my very best story of the Princess who knew how to use her own hands. I assure you, I learn a great deal by this exercise and am astonished at the impression it makes on the children. If I invent a trifling incident at one time and forget it at another, they instantly cry out that it was not so before, so that I am obliged to repeat my stories with an unchanging fidelity in substance and manner, which gives them the appearance of a monotonous recitative. I have learnt from this why the second edition of a tale with alterations cannot seem so good to us as the first, even if the alterations are improvements. The first impression is eagerly received and we believe any thing, however extravagant, but it has penetrated so deeply that he will meet only defeat and disgrace who attempts to change or obliterate it.

Aug. 18

Must the source of our happiness still be the source of our misery?

The overflowing sensibility of my heart to the beauties of nature, which once filled me with delight and spread an imaginary Paradise about me, has now become an intolerable persecutor, a foul demon, that haunts me wherever I go. Once when I gazed from the rocks on the luxuriant meadow, which stretches from the other side of the river to the hills and saw every thing there quickening into life and fertility—when I saw the mountains covered with venerable trees from their foundations to their summits, and the vallies shaded with smiling woods through all their various windings—when I saw the gentlest of rivers flowing among its whispering reeds and reflecting the light clouds, which the evening's breeze bore across the sky—when I listened to the birds who filled the woods around me with life and joy and watched the numberless insects, who were sporting in the last ruddy ray of that sun, whose parting beam released the droning beetle from his prison—when I observed the proofs of life which were spread every where around me, the moss that forced its nourishment from the unyielding rock on which I sat, and the broom that flourished on the parching sand-hill—*then* I seemed to witness the secret and vivifying and hallowed operations of Nature—*then* my heart was filled with her own penetrating and purifying warmth, and the awful image of the eternal world rose into life and reality before me. Solemn mountains surrounded me—precipices spread before me—torrents rushed by me—rivers swept at my feet—and hills and forests echoed with the uproar. I saw the kindly powers of Nature in perpetual activity in the unfathomable depths of the earth, while on its surface and under its sky myriads of living creatures walked and flew. All, *all* is peopled with the numberless tribes of life—and man shuts himself up in his narrow cell and proudly proclaims himself the tyrant of all! Miserable fool! whose very ignorance is the foundation of his imagined empire! From the unapproached and inaccessible mountain over the desert to the farthest limit of the unexplored ocean, the spirit of the Almighty is every where present and fills with joy whatever he has inspired with understanding and life. O, how often would I have flown on the wings of the eagle that passed over my head to the shore of that unmeasured ocean, where I could drink the waters of peace from the cup of immortality and, though but for an instant, feel in my languishing heart the pure happiness of that Eternal Being who created and sustains all things.

The mere memory of an hour like this renews my strength. The very effort to recall and explain these unutterable feelings raises my soul above itself but leaves me afterwards only a keener perception of my immediate misery.

But the scene is changed and instead of the vision of eternal life I see before me only an unfathomable abyss, an universal grave. Can you say that any thing exists, where every thing is passing away, where every thing is borne on a headlong torrent and the whole force of our nature is rarely sufficient to prevent us from being driven and dashed against the rocks? Every moment is wasting you and every thing around you—every moment you are and must be a destroyer. The most innocent walk is enjoyed at the expence of the lives of a thousand unfortunate insects—a single step may crush the edifice which has cost the ant so much patience and toil, and change a world to a grave. Oh no! it is not the tremendous and infrequent convulsions of the world—it is not the inundation or the earthquake, tho' it bury a city in ruins—it is not *this* that fills me with anguish. It is that dark principle of dissolution which mines unseen through all the works of nature—it is *this* that fills me with anguish. Heaven and earth with all their activity and energy surround me, yet I can see nothing but a frightful monster forever devouring and forever disgorging.

Aug. 21

I stretch out my arms in vain towards her when I awake in the morning from a troubled dream—I seek her in vain at midnight, when a bright and innocent vision has persuaded me that I sat by her in the meadow and held her hand and covered it with kisses. O, when in a doubtful sleep I seem hastening to meet her and then suddenly awake—a flood of tears bursts from my burthened heart and I weep like a child over sorrows that are yet to come.

Aug. 22

My active powers, my dear William, have degenerated into an uneasy indolence.

I cannot labour and I cannot endure to be idle. I have lost my skill in painting and my sensibility to the beauties of nature, and my books, too, weary me. When we are wanting to ourselves, every thing else is wanting to us. By heaven! I often wish I earned my daily bread by daily labour, only that I might rise in the morning with an object, an occupation, a hope! I often envy Albert, as he sits buried in parchments and imagine that if I were in his place I should be happy! Nay, I have often been so extravagant as almost to resolve to write to you and the minister for the place with the Ambassador, which you assure me would not be refused. I believe it. The minister has loved me long and urged me to ask for a place, and I have sometimes half a mind to do it. But when I think of it a second time and recollect the fable of the horse who grew weary of his freedom and suffered himself to be saddled and brideled and reduced to hard labour—I know not what I ought to do. And after all, William, may not this desire of change be only the consequence of a constitutional, restless impatience, which will still pursue me, wherever I may go?

Aug. 28

Surely, if there were any cure for my disease, such friends would afford it. To-day is my birth-day, and early this morning I received a packet from Albert. The first thing that caught my eye when I opened it was one of the pink knots which Charlotte wore the first time I saw her and which I asked her to give me some time ago. There were with it two duodecimo volumes—the little Wetstein Homer—a present which was particularly agreeable to me, as I have found the Ernesti too large for a walking companion. This ingenuity of kindness, which springs from genuine affection and anticipates our *little* wants is a thousand times more touching than those gorgeous presents which prove nothing but the vanity of the giver. I kissed the ribban a thousand times and with every breath drew in the recollection of the few happy, irrevocable days that passed so rapidly away. It is indeed so, William, but still I do not murmur. The flowers of life are faithless— most of them wither and leave no trace behind—of the remainder how few yield us any fruit—and of the fruit, how little ripens!

Evon of this, howevei, theie is enough—but to leave it, in its maturity and perfection—O my dear William!—to leave it unplucked and untasted—!

Farewell! It is a fine summer. I often go into Charlotte's garden and gather the pears from the tree, while she stands under it and catches them as I drop them to her.

Aug. 30

Am I not beside myself? Do I not deceive myself? What can this ardent, inextinguishable passion portend? I can offer up no prayers but for *her*—no form but *her's* rises to my imagination —and I think of the world and all that it contains only as it relates and tends to *her*. And this gives me many an hour of happiness—till I recollect that the time will come when I must tear myself from her. O, William, this thought fills me with the bitterest anguish!

When I have sat for hours together at her side and gazed on her form and watched her motions and listened to the enchantment of her conversation, by degrees my senses fade, my eyes grow dim, her accents die away on my ears* and my power of articulation is suffocated—then my heart labours in convulsive pulsations to relieve the oppression of my senses but only increases the confusion—William, at such moments I know not whether I am in the world or out. And when grief triumphs, as it sometimes does, and Charlotte allows me to pour out all my sorrows before her—I can endure it no longer—I rush forth from the house and find consolation in wandering through the fields or toiling up the mountain, or forcing my path through the trackless wood among bushes that oppose me and thornes that tear my flesh. And this gives me *some* comfort! *some!* And at last, perhaps, through weariness and thirst I throw myself on the earth—perhaps at the dead of night and in the solitude of a forest, with the full moon above me, I sit down at the foot of some old, fantastick tree to rest my wearied and wounded feet and there sink into the sleep of fatigue and forget myself till dawn—! O William! William! the dreary solitude of a convent, its penance and vigils, would seem like refreshment and repose after such sufferings! Farewell! my sorrows will end only in the grave.

Sep. 3

Yes, I must go—I thank you, my dear William, for deter-

---

* Sappho. [Ticknor's footnote. Ed.]

mining my doubtful resolution. For fourteen days I have suffered in perpetual anticipation the pangs of parting—I must go. She is now in town with a friend—and Albert—and I must go.

Sep. 10

What a night! William, it is all over! I shall never see her again! O, William, why cannot I throw myself on your bosom and with tears and triumph tell you all the feelings that are warring in my heart! I am sitting here panting for breath, labouring to compose myself, waiting for the morning, and at sunrise shall be gone!—

But *she* sleeps in peace and does not dream that she shall never see me again. I have torn myself from her and had the firmness to conceal my purpose during a conversation of two hours—and gracious God! *what* a conversation!

Albert had promised to meet me in the garden at twilight with Charlotte. I stood on the terrace under the chestnut trees and for the last time saw the sun shed his parting beam on the valley and the river. We had often stood together on this very spot and together witnessed the same glorious spectacle, and now—!

I walked up and down the alley that was so dear to me. A secret, sympathetick attraction had drawn me here before I knew Charlotte, and how did we rejoice, when, in the dawn of our acquaintance, we found that our mutual attachment dwelt on this spot! It is, indeed, one of the most romantick spots I ever saw even on canvass. In the first place, you have an extensive view between the chestnut trees—but I have told you all this very often before—I have told you how the beech trees gradually thicken and the copse closes and the alley grows darker and darker, until at last it terminates in a secret recess, which seems to be hidden in the very depths of solitude. The delight I felt the first time I entered this recess is still present to my imagination, and I still feel the melancholy forebodings which then seemed to warn me that it was destined to be the scene both of my happiness and misery.

I had passed about half an hour in these touching reflections and anticipations, when I heard them coming up the terrace. I ran to meet them and trembled as I took her hand and kissed it. When we had reached the top, we saw the moon rising from behind the trees on the hill. We talked on many subjects, and, before we thought of it, approached the recess. Charlotte went in and sat down and Albert and myself sat down by her. But I was not calm enough to sit long. I got up, walked to and fro, and sat down again. It was a fearful trial. She pointed us to the beautiful tints and shades produced by the light of the moon, which illuminated the whole terrace before us, at the end of the copse. It was a glorious exhibition, and much more striking from the darkness in which we were involved. We were silent, and after some time Charlotte said, "I never, *never* walk by moonlight without recalling to my thought the memory of those who were dear to me and who are no more—without thinking on death and eternity. We certainly shall live again," she added in a voice touched with the deepest tones of tenderness—"we certainly shall live again, but, Werter, shall we discover, shall we know each other? What are your presentiments?—what can you say?"

"Charlotte," said I, taking her hand and bursting into tears, "we shall see each other again both here and hereafter"—I could not finish what I had intended to say. —O, my dear William, how *could* she ask me such a question when my heart was bursting with the thought of separation!

"And can the purified spirits of those we love," said Charlotte, "look down and know us? Can they feel that in the hour of happiness we still remember them with a more tender affection. O, the form of my mother *does* hover over me, when, in the stillness of the evening, I sit surrounded by *her* children, by *my* children, when they gather about me, as they used to gather about herself —when I pray to heaven with anxious tears that she may be suffered though but for a moment to witness the fulfilment of the promise I gave her to the hour of death, that I would be a mother to her children. O, with what earnestness I cry: Pardon me, my mother, pardon me, that I am not every thing to them you were— I strive for them with all my strength—they are still fed and clothed—and what is above all this, they are still cherished and loved. Blessed spirit, could you see our harmony and peace, you would pour out your heart in gratitude to that God, to whom you poured out your last bitter tears and prayers for the happiness of your children."

She said more than this, William, but who can repeat what she said? How can a cold and lifeless page receive the living and glowing spirit of genius?

Albert gently interrupted her, "You are too much moved by it, my dear Charlotte, your mind dwells too much on these recollections—I beg you—" "O Albert," said she, "I know you do not forget the evenings we passed together at the little round table when my father was out and the children were put to bed. You often held a book in your hand, but how little you read!— for was not an intercourse with such a liberal spirit better than all that books can give? God is witness to the tears with which I wet my pillow, when I humbly pray to him that he would make me like my mother."

"Charlotte!" I exclaimed, and threw myself before her and seized her hand and wet it with my tears, "the blessing of Almighty God, and of your mother's purified spirit rests upon you!" "If you could but have known her!" said she and pressed my hand, "for she was worthy to be known even by you." I was motionless. Never had I received praise so unmeasured and yet so delicate. "And she was torn from us," said Charlotte, "in the prime of life, when her youngest darling was hardly six months old. Her illness was short. She was calm and resigned and anxious for nothing but her children and especially the youngest. As she approached the grave, she asked me to bring the children to her. The youngest were ignorant of their loss, and the eldest were overwhelmed by it. I still see them standing round her bed, while she raised her hands and prayed for them—I still see her receive each of them separately and give to each her last embrace—I still hear her dying injunction: 'Be a mother to them'—and still remember the solemn assurance of my obedience. 'You promise a great deal, my child,' said she, 'when you promise a mother's love and a mother's care. I have often seen your affection in your grateful tears. Let that affection rest on my children, and let your father find that you are to him as a faithful and attentive wife. You must be his comforter.' She asked for him, but he had gone out to conceal the sorrow he could not restrain and which had completely subdued him.

"You were in the chamber, Albert. She heard some one move and asked who it was and desired you to come to her. And then, when she saw us together, with a look of tranquil pleasure, which spoke her assurance that we should be happy—happy in each other—" Albert caught her in his arms and exclaimed, "We *are* happy, Charlotte, and we *shall* be."—Yes, even the calm Albert was moved, and as for me, I was completely beside myself.

"And such a woman, Werther, could die!" said she. "O God, I sometimes think with despair that the dearest objects of our love are torn from us and that it is the children who feel the loss most severely and complain the longest that the black men have carried away their mama!"

She rose to go. I started and trembled, but still kept my seat and still detained her hand. "We are going," said she. "It is time." She attempted to withdraw her hand, but I only held it the more earnestly. "We shall meet again," I cried, "we shall discover and know each other under every form. I go, I go willingly, but if it were forever, I could not, *could* not endure it. Farewell, Charlotte—farewell, Albert. We shall meet again"—"Yes, to-morrow, I fancy," said Charlotte playfully. That word 'to-morrow' went to my heart. O, she did not know, when she drew her hand from mine—I looked after them, till they had gone down the alley, and then threw myself on the earth and wept aloud—started up, ran to the terrace, and could still see the waving of her white gown under the lime-trees as she passed the garden-gate. I stretched out my arms towards her, and she disappeared.

The Sorrows of Young Werter
Book Second

Oct. 20. 1771

We arrived here yesterday. The ambassador is unwell and therefore will not go out for some days. If he were not so ill-humored, every thing would go very well. But I see plainly enough that I am reserved for hard trials. However, good courage! A light heart will carry me through all my troubles. A light heart! —It is amusing that I should have used such a phrase—and yet a little leaven of gaiety would make me the happiest man under the sun! What!—when other men with their meagre portion of energy and talent strut by me in the full enjoyment of their own self-importance, shall *I* distrust *my* powers and endowments? Almighty God! who hast been so bountiful to me, why was not the half of thy beneficence withheld, and vanity and self-complacency bestowed in its stead?

But patience! and I hope it will be better. You are right, my dear friend. Since I have been jostled about among the crowd and observed their conduct and motives, I am better satisfied with myself. It is certainly true that since we are so formed as to be perpetually influencing each other, and perpetually assimilating in our characters, the happiness or misery of every individual is essentially connected with circumstances in which he is placed, and that nothing is more fatal to our peace than solitude. There the imagination, which naturally tends to extravagance, is fed on the unsubstantial dreams of poetry and forms for itself a new creation, in which man is placed in the lowest rank and every thing about and above him seems more noble and perfect than himself. This is very natural. We often feel that many things are wanting to us, and precisely what we want seems to be possessed by another to whom we attribute all *we* have and add to it a fancied permanency—so the perfectly happy man is but the creature of our own imagination.

On the contrary, if notwithstanding all our own weakness and all the obstacles that oppose us we only strive to move directly forward, we shall at last find that our persevering labour will have carried us further towards our object than our neighbour has gone with all his sails and tacticks.—In this way, too, a man will find his own place, and whether it be above or below those around him.

Nov. 26

I begin to find my situation here quite tolerable. The best part of it, however, is that I have enough to do. And then the multitude and variety of characters that are continually passing before me form a most amusing spectacle.

I have become acquainted with count C————, a man whom I honour more and more every day, a man of uncommon talents and of a wide circumspection and yet of an affectionate temper—a man who you instantly see is formed for friendship and love. He took an interest in me when I met him on some business and perceived, from the first word I spoke, that we understand each other and that he could talk to me with a freedom which he must not show to many. I cannot sufficiently admire his frankness towards me, for indeed there is no higher pleasure than that of enjoying the unreserved confidence of a great mind.

Dec. 24

The ambassador is as troublesome as I anticipated he would be. He is the most punctilious of all blockheads—moves step by step with all the canting formality of an old woman—and is never contented with himself or grateful to any body else. I go rapidly through my business, and when it is done, it is done; but when I have given him my draught he returns it, saying: "It is very well, but go over it once more, for you can always find a better word or a more appropriate particle." I lose all patience. Not an 'if' or and 'and' escapes his criticism, and as for the inversions in which I sometimes indulge myself, they are so many deadly sins, and if every period is not adjusted exactly according to his own monotonous style, he will have nothing to do with it. It is indeed a curse to have any thing to do with such a man.

The society of Count C———— is my only comfort. He told me the other day, with a great deal of frankness, that he could not abide the tediousness and formality of my ambassador. "Such people," said he, "are a torment to themselves and every body about them, and yet we should not complain of them any more than a traveller should complain of being obliged to cross a mountain. To be sure, if the mountain were not there the road would be shorter and more pleasant, but since it *is* there he has nothing to do but to go over it."

The ambassador sees that the Count prefers me to him, and this vexes him, and he seizes every opportunity to speak ill of the count to me. I very naturally answer him and so the breach between us widens every day. Yesterday he assailed him in such a way as to hit me at the same time. "In the ordinary intercourse of society," said he, "the count gets along well enough. He has a considerable facility in business, and a pleasant style, but, like all belle-lettres scholars, he is superficial." And then he gave me a look which asked me plainly enough: Do you feel it? But it failed of its intended effect upon me, for I could only despise the man who could thus think and act. However, I opposed him and answered with apparent warmth: That the Count was a man who deserved to be equally honoured for his talents and for his worth. "I have never known a man," said I, "in whom there was so happy an union of commanding talents, with a power of descending to the minutest details, and a perpetual activity in the common business of life." This was all Greek to him, and I broke off the conversation to prevent farther collision from producing farther bitterness.

And it is *you* who are to answer for all this, for *you* persuaded me to wear the galling yoke by perpetually preaching to me about activity. *Activity*? Why, if the peasant who plants his potatoes and carries his corn to market is not more active than I am, I will willingly labour ten years more at the galley to which I am now chained.

What splendid misery and ennui there is among the fashionable society here! What an ambition of precedence!—what a perpetual vigilance and eagerness to surpass each other!—a melancholy and contemptible passion, which they have not sense enough even to conceal. There is a woman here, for instance, who can talk of nothing but her ancestors and estates so that a stranger could not imagine her to be any thing but a weak woman, whose head had been turned by her forefathers and her fortune. But it is, in fact, much worse, for she is nothing but the daughter of a neighbouring steward's secretary. I cannot imagine how people can be so totally void of understanding as to disgrace themselves in this way.

It is true, my dear William, that I every day see more and more clearly the folly of measuring others by ourselves, and as long as I have so much to reform in my own character and as long as my own heart is so full of tumult and trouble, I can easily persuade myself to suffer other people to travel quietly

forward in the path they have chosen, if they will but let me go
on in mine.

Nothing vexes me more than the absurd distinctions that pre-
vail here. I know very well that there must be a diversity of ranks
in society, and have myself felt its advantages, but I would not
have it mar a moment's enjoyment or interrupt a single ray of
that happiness which would otherwise reach the earth.

I lately met on the publick walk a Miss B———, a most interesting woman, who has preserved the openness of her disposition in defiance of the forms of fashionable life. We were
pleased with each other's conversation and when we parted I
asked her permission to visit her. She granted it so cordially
that I could hardly wait for the appointed time to call on her. She
is not a native of this place and is now living at the house
of an aunt. I did not much like the old lady's physiognomy, but
I was very attentive to her, addressed the greater part of my
conversation to her and in less than half an hour suspected what
the niece has since confessed, that in her old age, without attractions or talent, she has no support but her ancestry, no defense but
the pride of birth with which she surrounds herself as with a
pallisade, and no amusement but to look down from her window
upon the heads of the plodding citizens who pass by. In her
youth she was handsome, and she has wasted her life, first in
vanity and coquetry and afterwards in her riper years under the
discipline of an old officer, who enjoyed his prize and a comfortable estate, till he reached about fifty and then died—and
now, if she had not so interesting a niece, she would live in un-
consoled and unnoticed solitude.

Jan. 8. 1772

What name of contempt do those men deserve, the whole of
whose thoughts are occupied with form and ceremony—whose
address and activity is spent for a year together in contriving
to advance themselves nearer to the head of the table by a single
chair. And this is not because they have nothing else to occupy
them, for a man here will allow his business to increase into
cureless confusion, rather than neglect his pretensions to precedence. Last week a sleigh-ride was broken up by one of these
contemptible disputes.

It is a remarkable folly which will not see the difference between substantial greatness and apparent rank, and does not

know that he who fills the first place seldom plays the first part. Is not a king often governed by his minister and the minister by his secretary? And which of these is first? Surely he who has the widest circumspection, and whose energy or artifice can direct the talents and passions of the rest to his own purposes.

Jan. 20

I must write to you, my dear Charlotte—I must write to you from this cottage, in which I have taken refuge from a violent storm. While I was driven to and fro in the melancholy city of D——— among strangers—strangers at least to my feelings —there was not a moment, a *single* moment in which my heart called on me to write to you, and yet *here,* in this cabin, in this solitary, cheerless apartment, while the snow and hail are rattling against my narrow window—*here* you were my first thought. The moment I entered *here,* your form, Charlotte, your bright and hallowed form rose into life before me. Gracious God! I thank thee for having vouchsafed me another hour of happiness!

If you could but see me, Charlotte, tossed on the flood of dissipation—if you could but see the desolation of my heart—not a moment of the overflow of feeling—not a single hour of blessed peace—nothing! nothing! I stand as if at a raree-show, and see men of all conditions pass in review before me, and often question with myself if it is not all an optical delusion? I even mingle with the machinery and am moved and managed like the rest of the puppets and sometimes seize the hand of the one that stands next to me and shudder to find that it is but wood!

In the evening I promise myself the enjoyment of sunrise and yet I do not get up. During the day I look forward to a walk by moonlight and yet in the evening I do not leave my chamber. I go to bed without a motive and rise without a hope. The spring which gave an impulse and direction to my life is broken. The spell which made my midnight hours hours of watchfulness is gone. The vision which chased my morning slumbers has vanished!

I have found but a single kindred spirit of your sex here, a Miss B———. She would be like you, my dear Charlotte, if it were possible that any body could be like you. "Ah, ha," you will say, "he has learnt to make fine compliments." Truly, I fear, you are right. I have for some time been very gallant because I am fit for nothing else—have cultivated a very pretty wit— and the women give me the praise of being very happy in a compliment—(and in a falsehood you will add, for what is a compliment without falsehood?). However I am talking of Miss B——. She has a great deal of feeling, which beams from her fine blue eyes. Her rank is a burthen which she knows not how to enjoy. She sighs for peace and quiet, and we often make our own world for hours together in rural life amidst scenes of unmingled happiness—scenes, Charlotte, in which you bear a part. O, how often is she obliged to do homage to you—no, not *obliged*, for she does it freely, delights to hear me talk of you, and loves you herself.

Would to heaven I could again sit at your feet in that chosen parlour and again have the children romping about me, and, if they made too much noise, again quiet them by a touching story.

The sun has just burst forth upon the fields glittering with snow—the storm is over—and I—*I* must return to my prison. Farewell! Is Albert with you? And in what relation? God forgive me for asking such a question!

Feb. 8

For a week past we have had most dismal weather and it has almost made me happy again, for there has not been a single fine day since I have been here which some untoward blockhead has not spoiled for me. But when it rains and snows and freezes and thaws, then I am sure it is as pleasant in the house as it is abroad, and therefore I am content. If the sun rises in the morning and promises a fair day, I cannot help exclaiming: There you have another of God's blessings, which you will pervert to each other's misery. There is nothing which you do not thus pervert. Health, reputation, happiness, every thing is abused by your folly and selfishness, and, if *you* are to be believed, with the best intentions. O, I could throw myself on my knees before them and beseech them not to strive thus against their own dearest interests.

Feb. 17

I am afraid I shall not be able to go on with this ambassador much longer. The fellow is absolutely intolerable. His mode of doing business is so truly absurd that I cannot always restrain myself from contradicting him and doing it in my own way. This, of course, vexes him and he has complained of it at court— the consequence of which is that the minister has sent me a reprimand—very mild, I know, but still a reprimand—and I was on the point of asking a dismission, when I received a private letter from him—a letter before which I humbled myself and offered up my gratitude to the elevated and liberal and powerful mind that dictated it. He understands my excessive sensibility, and speaks with flattering respect of my enlarged ideas of business and of my influence and activity as well-suited to my years —and tells me not to exterminate but to restrain and direct them to their natural field and proper objects. This has determined me to remain a week longer and has besides reconciled me to myself. A contented temper is a pearl of great price, but, my dear friend, the jewel is as frail as it is beautiful and precious.

Feb. 20

God bless you, my dear friends, and add to your lives all the happy days he takes from mine.

I thank you, Albert, for deceiving me. I supposed I should have learnt beforehand when you would be married and I had determined on that day formally to take down Charlotte's profile from the wall and bury it among my other papers. But you are married and it is still here! Here then let it remain! And why not? I know that I have a right in Charlotte's heart, on which you do not intrude—yes, I know that I have the second place there, and I *will* not, *can* not lose it! O, I should grow frantick if it were possible she could forget—! Albert! there is perdition in that thought! Farewell Albert! Angel of light, Charlotte, farewell!—

March 15

An incident has occurred which makes my farther residence here impossible. I have lost all patience! However, it is all over now, and the fault is to be charged entirely to you—*you*, who have driven and goaded and tormented me into a place for which my very nature rendered me unfit. Now attend, and you shall have it, and that you may not again say, I exaggerate and discolour every thing, you shall have it set down, my dear Sir, in as plain, unvarnished a tale as history ever recorded.

Count C——— likes me, notices me, as is publickly known and as I have told you an hundred times. Yesterday I dined with him, and it happened to be the day of the evening on which all the gentry assemble there—a circumstance which did not enter into my thoughts any more than that we subalterns have no part or place in their honourable assemblies. Well, I dined with the Count and after dinner walked up and down the hall in conversation with him and Colonel B———, who happened to call,

until at last the hour came for the party to meet. All this time,
however, Heaven knows, I thought of nothing. First the Honourable Mrs. S——— with her formal husband and foolish daughter
came in and swept by me with a look of lofty contempt. As I
have no particular regard for such sort of people, I was only
waiting for the Count to be relieved from their stupid conversation, in order to make my bow, when Miss B——— came in.
Now, as my heart is always a little moved by her presence, I
stopped as soon as I saw her and went up behind her chair. In
a few moments I observed that she spoke to me with less freedom
and ease than usual and, in fact, with considerable embarassment. I was hurt by it. "Can she be like the rest of the world?"
said I—and I was offended and again determined to go, but still
I remained to find some excuse for her, hoping it might be a mistake and that her natural manner would return and that—
in short, I stayed for any thing or nothing.

In the mean time the company continued to assemble. Baron
F——— came in bearing about a whole wardrobe as old as the
coronation of Francis I. —Counsellor R ———, here known by
courtesy as Sir R———, with his dull wife, etc. etc., not to
forget the half-clad J———, who mends the tatters of his anti-
que French dresses with remnants of modern fashions. I talked
with several of my acquaintance who were all quite laconick, I
thought, but in fact I observed only Miss B———. I did not ob-
serve that the ladies at the end of the room were all whispering
—that the contagion had spread to the gentlemen—that Mrs.
S——— was in conversation with the count (all which Miss
B——— has since told me), until at last he came up to me and
drew me aside into a recess. "You are aware," said he, "of the
singularity of our customs. The company is disturbed, I see,
by your being here. I would not for the world—" "I beg your
Excellency's pardon a thousand times," said I interrupting him.
"I ought to have recollected it, but I am sure you will forgive my
forgetfulness. I intended to have gone earlier, but some evil genius
has detained me," said I, smiling as I made my bow. The Count
shook my hand with a cordiality which expressed more than
words. I bowed to the honourable company, retired, jumped into
a cabriolet and rode over to M——— to watch the setting sun and
read in my Homer the exquisite story of Ulysses' entertainment
by the swineherds. So far, all was very well.

In the evening I returned home and found a few still in the

supper-hall, who were playing at dice on a corner of the table, from which they had thrown back the cloth. Mr. A——— came in and laid down his hat, and when he observed me came up to me and whispered: "You have had an unpleasant adventure?" "Me?" said I. "The count sent you away from the party." "You're confoundedly mistaken," said I. "I went out to take the fresh air." "I am glad you consider the matter so lightly. It is a pity people are beginning to talk about it." The thing now began to disturb me. Every body that came to the table and noticed me seemed, as I imagined, to look at me with impertinent inquisitiveness, and this added to my vexation. And, wherever I go to-day, I meet condolence and sympathy, because my enemies have obtained such a triumph and can say, "This is always the way with vain men, who endeavour to rise above their proper level, and one presumptuous enough to despise the proprieties of life." I had as lief a man should thrust a poignard in my heart. Say what you will of independence, but show me the man who can preserve his patience while scoundrels are assailing him, who have him in their power. When their malice is impotent, it is easily endured.

March 16

Every thing conspires to vex me. Yesterday I met Miss B——— on the publick walk and could not help speaking to her and telling her—as soon as we were out of the reach of the company— my mortification at her late conduct. "O Werter," said she in a tone of deep feeling, "is it possible you could so interpret my embarassment, and yet know my heart? You do not suspect how much I suffered for you from the moment you entered the room. I foresaw it all and was an hundred times on the point of telling it to you. I knew that the S's and T's with their husbands would leave the room rather than remain in your company, and I knew, too, that the Count could not offend them. And now the talk there is about it!" "What talk?" said I, concealing my emotion, for all that Adelin had told me now poured like scalding lead through my veins. "O, what has it not already cost me," said she, and the tears stood in her eyes. I was no longer master of myself and would gladly have thrown myself at her feet. "Explain yourself," said I. The tears ran down her cheeks and I was beside myself. She wiped them away without attempting to conceal them. "My aunt," she went on, "was present, you know, and saw your conduct with the eyes of prejudice. O Werter, I had such a sermon last night and this morning on my acquaintance with you!—and was obliged to hear you degraded and insulted without being able and without daring more than half to defend you."

Every word she uttered went through my heart. She knew not how merciful it would have been to conceal it from me—and now she went on to show me what was to follow, what sort of people would triumph over me, and how they would rejoice at this punishment of the insolence and superciliousness with which they have so long reproached me and how merry they would make themselves at my expence. All this, William, I was obliged to hear from her in a tone of unaffected interest—I was furious and am still hardly more composed. I longed to have some one dare to cast the odious reproach upon me, that I might take vengeance on his life—for if I could once see blood I should feel better. O! I have an hundred times seized a dagger to give peace to my troubled heart! There is said to be a species of high-spirited horses, who when they are overheated in the race tear open a voin by instinct and relieve their breath. It is often so with me—if I would but open a vein I might receive a perpetual release.

March 24

I have asked for my dismission at court and hope to obtain it. You must forgive me that I did not first consult you, but I had made up my mind that I could stay no longer, and I knew very well beforehand all you could say to persuade me to remain. Tell my mother, and tell her tenderly, that I am hardly sufficient for myself, and that she will but fall, if she leans on such a broken reed. Indeed, it will be a sore affliction to her to see her son so suddenly stopped in his bright course to the rank of a councillor or ambassador and returned to his original insignificance.

Now, then, you may make what you will of the the case and combine if you please all the possible circumstances under which I could and ought to have remained, for I am determined to go, and that you may know my destination, I tell you that the Prince of ——— is here, that he likes me, and that as soon as he knew my resolution he invited me to go to his estate and pass the spring there. He has promised me I shall be left entirely to myself, and as we understand one another tolerably well, I shall trust to fortune and go with him.

Postscript.   *April 19*

I thank you for your two letters. You had no answer because I have detained it till I have received my dismission from court, fearing my mother might write to the minister and obstruct my wishes. But now it is all over, and my dismission is before me. I will not tell you how reluctantly it was given or what the minister wrote me, for it would only increase your regret. The Prince sent me five and twenty ducats on my resignation, with an expression of kindness which moved me even to tears. Of course I do not want the money for which I wrote to my mother.

May 5

I shall set off to-morrow, and as the place where I was born is but six miles out of my way, I shall visit it once more and once more recall the happy days and dreams of my childhood. I will go in at the very door from which my mother led me out when she left this cherished spot after the death of my father to bury her sorrows in her native village. Farewell, William. You shall have an account of my excursion.

May 9

I performed my excursion to the place of my birth with all the devotion of a Pilgrim, and, in the course of it, had many an unexpected feeling awakened. I stopped under the large lime-tree that stands a quarter of a league from the town and told the postillion to go on, that by entering the place on foot I might revive every impression with more force and reality. I stood still under this lime-tree, which in my childish days had been the extent and limit of my walks. How changed! *Then* I looked forth in blessed ignorance on an unknown world, where my heart trusted to find support and happiness—where my aspiring and ambitious hopes would be fulfilled and satisfied. *Now*, I had returned from this wide world—O my dear friend!—returned with disappointed hopes and unsucceeded plans. I looked towards the mountain, which was stretched before me, and which I had so often considered the barrier to my wishes. I could then sit here by hours together and sigh to wander among the refreshing shades of its woods and valleys—and, when the appointed hour called me to return, with what lingering reluctance I left the cherished spot! I approached the town and was delighted to see again the arbours that had been familiar to me, but the new ones

and all the other changes offended me. I entered the village and
felt that I was once more at home. I will not go into the details
of my visit, for however happy it might have been, in fact, it
would be but dull on paper.

I had determined to lodge in the market near our former
home. As I went towards it, I observed that the schoolhouse in
which a reverend beldame used to instruct our childhood was
changed to a shop. I remember well the toil, the tears, the mortifications, the heart-aches I suffered there.

Every step I advanced was the scene of adventure. A Pilgrim
in Palestine would not find so many monuments consecrated by
religious recollections or enjoy more high and holy feelings. Take
a single instance. Passing along a little brook towards a farm-
house—in a path I used to frequent and where, when we were
children, we used to play at ducks and drakes—I instantly recollected how I used to gaze on that water, with what earnestness
of imagination I followed its course, how full of adventure I
fancied the countries through which it was to pass—until I found
too soon that my invention was exhausted, but still I was urged
forward farther and farther until all had vanished in the dimness
of distance.

This, my dear friend, was the happy ignorance of our glorious
forefathers. This was the child-like simplicity of their feelings
and their poetry. When Ulysses talks of the immeasurable
ocean and the boundless earth, does he not speak to our natural
feelings and personal convictions and experience? And what
does it profit me that with every school-boy I can say by rote
that the earth is round? A man needs but little of this earth for
his subsistence and still less for his final home.

I am now with the Prince at his hunting-lodge and live very
pleasantly with him, for he is true-hearted and open. There are
some singular men about him, whom I do not much admire. They
do not seem to be altogether knaves or absolutely honest. Sometimes they seem very disinterested, but still I cannot give them
my confidence. What offends me most is that he often speaks of
things, of which he has only heard or read, with as much posi-
tiveness and precision as if he could have seen them with another's eyes.

He places a higher value on my understanding and talents
than on that heart which is my only wealth—which is the solitary

source of my faculties, my joys, my sorrows—every thing! Oh, the little I know may be learned by any man, but my heart—*that* is all my own.

May 25

I had a project in my head, which I did not intend to have explained to you until I had executed it, but as it has failed altogether, I may just as well explain it to you now. I have for a long time earnestly desired to join the army. This is the reason I came here with the Prince, who is a General in the service of —————. Taking a walk with him, I explained my plan. He opposed it, and I must have had much more of passion than of whim if I had not been convinced by his arguments.

June 11

Say what you will, I can stay here no longer. And why should I, since I am tired of it? The Prince, I know, treats me with the greatest kindness, but still I am not in my place. Besides, we have, at bottom, nothing in common. He is, to be sure, a man of understanding, but it is an understanding of an ordinary class. His conversation does not excite me more than a well-written book would. I shall remain here a week longer and then once more set forth on my wanderings.

The best thing I have done here is my paintings. The Prince has some taste in the arts and would have more, if he were not trammelled by scientifick rules and common-place technicks. He puts me out of all patience when he comes in upon me with one of his cold criticisms, which he thinks will set every thing to rights at the moment when I with my more ardent imagination am leading him forward into the secrets of art and nature.

June 16

Yes, I am but a wanderer and a pilgrim on the earth! Are you, then, more?

June 18

Where I mean to go? I will tell you in confidence. I must remain here a fortnight and then I mean to go and visit the mines in —————. But, in fact, it is no such thing—it is only that I may be somewhat nearer to Charlotte. I smile at the weakness of my heart, and then yield to it.

July 29

Oh, no! It is right—it is all right! *I* her husband? Almighty

God, who gavest me existence, if thou hadst bestowed upon me happiness like this, my whole life would have been one perpetual thanksgiving. But I will not complain. Forgive me these tears— forgive me these vain wishes! Charlotte my wife! Oh, if that loveliest of women had been given to my arms—! William! I am almost convulsed when Albert throws his arm round her slender waist!

And may I dare to say it? Why not, William? She would have been happier with me than with him. O, he is not the man who can satisfy all the wishes of her heart. He wants that full flow of feeling—he wants—call it what you please, but his heart does not beat in unison with her's, when, over a passage of a favourite author and in an hundred other cases where we happen to express our opinions, my heart and Charlotte's meet in sympathy.— Dear William, I know he loves her with undivided affection, and what does not such love deserve?

An insufferable visitor has interrupted me. My tears are dried and I am more composed. Farewell, my dear friend!—

Aug. 4

I am not solitary in suffering. All men are disappointed in their hopes and deceived in their expectations. I have just visited the good woman who lives by the lime-trees. The eldest child ran to meet me and by his exclamation of joy brought out his mother, who bore all the marks of deep sorrow. The first word she said was: "My sweet John is dead." He was the youngest of her boys. I made her no reply. "And my husband," she went on, "has returned from Switzerland without the property. He was sick of a fever on the road, and if it had not been for a few kind people he would have been obliged to beg his way home." I could not speak—but I gave the children something and took some apples that she offered me and left the place which is now associated with so many melancholy recollections.

Aug. 21

My life is a life of sudden changes. Sometimes a ray of joy gleams on me for a moment, but then it is *only* for a moment. When I forget myself, and lose the command over my thoughts, I sometimes say to myself, "What if Albert should die? You would—yes, I am sure she would—" and then I follow the thread of fancy, till it leads me to the very verge of the precipice and I recoil with horror.

If I pass along the same road which I passed for the first time when I carried Charlotte to the ball, I am struck with the fearful change. All, *all* has vanished—not a gleam of the gay world I then knew—not a pulsation of the joy which then swelled in my bosom! I feel all that would be felt by the departed spirit of a Prince who should revisit the ruins and wreck of a palace which he had built in the pride of youth and left to the son of his hopes and affections, hung with all the pomp of empire.

Sep. 3

Sometimes I am unable to comprehend how she *can* love another—how she *dares* to love another, while I am so dearly devoted to her, while I have no thought, no wish, that does not rest on her.

Sep. 4

Yes, it is so. The autumn which subdues nature, subdues, too, every thing around and within me. My May of life has fallen into the sear and yellow leaf, and the trees about me are equally bare and cheerless.

Did I not tell you, when I first came here, of a remarkable young peasant? I have been inquiring after him at Walheim and have learned that he has been sent away from the widow's service and supplanted in her affections by a rival, and that nobody knows what has become of him. * * * *

Sep. 5

She wrote a letter to her husband in the country, where he is employed on business. It began: "Do come back again, dearest, as soon as you can. I am looking forward to it with inexpressible delight—" A friend, who came in at this moment, told her that, from some circumstances, he would not return so soon. The letter remained unfinished and in the evening fell into my hands. I read it and smiled—She asked me why I smiled? "The imagination," said I, "is truly a gift from heaven. For an instant I fancied it might have been written to me." She changed the conversation. It seemed to have displeased her and I said no more.

Sep. 6

I have been obliged with reluctance to lay aside the plain blue frock, in which I danced with Charlotte the first time I saw her and which was at last unfit to be seen. But, I have had

another made exactly like it—buttons, trimmings and all—
and a [yellow] vest and smallclothes to match.

Still it does not produce the same effect upon me —I don't
know, but perhaps in time it will be as dear to me.

Sep. 12

She had been absent some days on an excursion to meet Albert.
To-day I went to see her. She met me in the entry and I kissed
her hand with heart-felt delight.

A canary bird flew from the mirror to her shoulder. "This
is a new friend," said she, taking him in her hand, "whom I
intend for the children. See, how affectionate he is! How he
claps his wings and how gently he pecks at me when I give him
bread! See! He kisses me,too!" And then she held her mouth
open to him and he dipped his bill in her lips as tenderly as if
he felt the happiness he enjoyed. "He shall kiss you, too," said
she, and gave the bird to me. He dipped the bill, which he had
just taken from her lips, in mine and its gentle pecking seemed
like a breathing and foretaste of unmingled happiness.

"His favours," said I, "are not entirely disinterested. He is
looking for his food and returns discontented if he obtains only a kiss." "O yes," said she, "he feeds from my lips, too." She
then gave him some crumbs from her mouth, which expressed,
in every movement and dimple, the most innocent and artless
delight.

I turned away my head. She should not do it—she ought not
to excite my imagination with such images of heavenly purity
and happiness, or awaken my heart from the sleep into which
the tranquillity of life sometimes lulls it. And why not? Does
she not treat me with this frankness because she knows how
truly I love her?

Sep. 15

It is enough to confound all patience, my dear William, to
think that there are people who have no sensibility or perception
to the few things in this world that are worthy of our affection.
You know the walnut trees, under which I sat with Charlotte
and the venerable curate of St. ——, the beautiful walnut trees,
which, heaven knows, it always did my heart good to look at—
which made the parsonage so retired and cool—whose branches
were so luxuriant—and whose history was dearly associated
with the recollections of the holy men of old who planted them.

The Schoolmaster has often told me of one of them whose story he had heard from his grandfather. He was a high minded man, and his memory has always been hallowed by me under these trees. I assure you, the tears stood in the Schoolmaster's eyes when he yesterday told me they were cut down. — *Cut down!* Why, I should have gone mad—I could have torn the wretch in my anger, who dared to strike the first blow! And yet *I* must endure all this, *I*, who could willingly have gone in mourning if two such trees had stood in my yard, and one of them had died of old age. Sweet trees! *one* is still spared to me!

Publick feeling is touched by it. The whole village murmurs against it, and I hope the curate's wife will learn from her diminished stock of butter and eggs and other presents, how gross an outrage she has committed. For it is *she*—it is the wife of the new curate (our old one is dead), an ill-favoured, haggard, fretful old creature, who has little cause to care about the world, since the world cares nothing about her—an ideot, too, who affects to be thought learned, joins in the controversy about the canons, interests herself in the new moral and critical reformation of Christianity, sneers at Lavater's idle fancies and has a broken constitution and a heart incapable of enjoying the blessings which God has poured around her—*this* is the miserable creature and the only one that could have found it in her heart to cut down my walnut-trees. And she did it, forsooth, because the leaves made the yard dirty and damp—because the trees interrupted the light—and because, when the nuts were ripe, the boys would throw stones at them, and this disturbs her nerves and interrupts her deliberations on the relative merit of Semler, and Kennicott, and Michaëlis. When I found the villagers and especially the old men so much moved by it, I said: "Why did you permit it?" "What can we do," said they, "when the superintendent issues his orders?" One thing, however, has happened very well. The superintendent and the curate, who, with accustomed submission, joined in his wife's plan, had intended to share the wicked profit, but the revenue-officer came in and said the government had outstanding claims on the parsonage where the trees grew and so sold them to the highest bidder. There they still lie!—O, if I were a king in the land, I would make the curate's wife and the superintendent and the revenue officer—A *King!* Why, if I were a king, what should I care about all the trees in my dominions?

Oct. 10

If I can but gaze on her dark eyes, I am happy! What grieves me is that Albert does not seem so happy as he—hoped he should be, as I—think I should be—if—. I do not often write in such broken sentences, but here I cannot explain myself in any other way—and the meaning, after all, seems to be sufficiently explicit.

Oct. 12

Ossian has taken the place of Homer in my heart. He leads me to a world of wonders indeed! I follow him in his wanderings over the heaths and through tempests on whose solemn clouds the spirits of his fathers ride forth in the pale light of the moon. I listen with him from the mountains, amidst the uproar of the storm, to the wailings of the dead in the depths of their caverns and to the sighs of the maiden, who pours out her sorrows and her life at the moss-covered tomb of her fallen hero and lover— I meet the aged bard on the wild, where he seeks the footsteps of his fathers and finds alas! only their graves!—I see him turn his disconsolate eye towards the mild star of evening as it sinks in the heaving ocean, and mark how it recalls to his proud spirit the days that are past, the days when its friendly ray lighted him to danger and glory and the moon shone on his bark as it returned with the spoils and garlands of victory. But when I read the deep despair which has settled on his brow—when I see the last of the fallen generation of greatness tottering in decrepitude to the tomb and finding his hope and happiness in that very decay which is the token of his release—when I see him gaze on the cold earth that is to cover him and the tall grass which is to wave over him, and hear him cry: "The traveller will come—he who saw me in the days of my beauty will come and ask: 'Where is the bard? Where is Fingal's honour'd son?' His footstep is on my grave—he seeks me in vain on the earth!"— *then,* William, *then* I could seize the sword of heroism and release my Prince from the languor of gradual decay and afterwards send forth my own emancipated spirit to accompany the Demigod!

Oct. 19

O, this void, this fearful void that I feel in my heart! I sometimes think that if I could once, *only* once press her to my bosom, this void would be filled.—

Oct. 26

Yes, my dear friend, I am every day more and more convinced that the life of any one individual is of little, very little conse- quence to society. A female friend came in to visit Charlotte, and I retired into this adjoining apartment to amuse the time with reading, but as I was not in the humour to read I took up a pen. I heard their conversation. They talked of strange accidents and village news—of this man's marriage and that man's illness, extreme illness. "He has a dry cough," said Charlotte's friend, "the bones have almost come through his skin, and he has con- tinual fainting-fits. I would not give a creutzer for his chance." "Mr. N—— is hardly in a better condition," said Charlotte. "No, he is swollen already," replied the visitor. My imagination im- mediately carried me to the chambers of these unfortunate be- ings—I saw the strong convulsions with which they struggled against dissolution—how they—O William! and yet Charlotte and her friend spoke of it as they would have spoken of the death of a stranger!—When I look about me and see this chamber and Charlotte's clothes and Albert's papers and the furniture and even this inkstand, with all which I am so familiar and intimate, and say to myself: What are you now to this family? You are every thing. Your friends honour you—you are a part of their system of happiness, which you fondly imagine would be im- paired if you were taken away, and yet if you were now to leave them—if you were to be this instant torn from their circle, how long, think you, how long would they feel the chasm which your absence had left? O it is hard that the heart should be so fickle! It is hard that there, where we felt the most intimate assurance of our happiness—there where we seemed to have made the deep- est and dearest impression on the memory and affections of those we love—that *there*, too, we should be forgotten and forgotten so quickly!

Oct. 27

I could tear open my bosom—I could dash out my brains, when I think that we are of so little consequence to each other. O, if I cannot offer a cordial and deep affection I must not ex- pect it in return—and with a disposition overflowing with kindness, I can never impart that happiness to another which a cold and insensible heart renders him unfit to enjoy.

Evening

I possess much, but the recollection of her absorbs it all—I possess much, but without her it would be nothing!—

Oct. 30

I have been an hundred times on the point of throwing my arms round her neck. God knows what a trial it is to see such charms continually passing before me without daring to touch them. And yet to touch what we love is the most natural thing in the world—Do not children touch whatever pleases them? And I—!

Nov. 3

Heaven knows how often I close my eyes with the wish and sometimes even with the hope that I may never awake, and in the morning return again to life and misery. Would to God I had a perverse disposition—that I could charge my sufferings to inclement seasons—to an enemy—to disappointed ambition, for then I should escape from half the intolerable burthen of self-reproach! But I feel too surely that the guilt is all my own—no! not guilt—say rather that my bosom is now the secret source of all my misery as it was once the source of all my happiness. Am not *I* the man who once passed on gay and happy—on whom Paradise opened at every step—and who had a heart that extended its kindness to the whole world! But that heart is dead, and enthusiasm dwells there no more. My eyes are dry, and my senses, which are no longer moistened with refreshing tears, constrain and oppress my troubled brain. My sufferings are great, for I have lost what was the sole delight of my life, the hallowed, active principle which enabled me to live in a world of my own imagination—that principle is gone!

When I look from my window towards the distant hills and see the rising sun bursting from the cloud that had settled on them and shining on the silent meadows—when I listen to the gentle river as it winds among its leafless willows—O, when all nature rises before me like a splendid vision, and all its pomp and jubilee strike a cold and unaffected heart—then I seem to stand before the face of heaven in churlish solitude like a parched fountain, like the blasted fig tree! Often have I thrown myself on the earth and besought my God for tears as the husbandman prays for rain, when the heavens over his head are as brass and the earth beneath his feet as powder. But alas! I feel, that God does not grant rain and sunshine to the vehemence of importunity, for why were those days so happy, the recollection of which now fills me with anguish, but because I waited with patience for his good pleasure and enjoyed with an open and grateful heart the happiness his bounty vouchsafed me.

Nov. 8

She has reproved me for my excesses—but with such tenderness!—my excesses! because now I sometimes drink a whole bottle instead of the single glass I used to drink. "Don't do so," said she, "remember Charlotte." "Remember?" said I. "Do you think it is necessary to *bid* me do that? *I* remember you? No, I cannot remember *you*—you who are *always* present to my tho'ts. To-day I was sitting on the stone on which you stepped when you got out of the coach the other day—." She changed the conversation to prevent me from going deeper into the subject. —O William, I am nothing now—she manages me as she pleases.

Nov. 15

I thank you, dearest William, for your kindness, for your honest advice—and beseech you not to be afflicted by my sorrows. Let me bear them alone, for, heavy as they are, my strength is still equal to my burthen.

You know I reverence religion—you know I am persuaded it is a staff to the aged and a balm to many a wounded spirit. But can it, must it be so to all? Look round the world and you will find thousands to whom it never was, and thousands to whom it never will be, whether it be preached to them or not—and *must* it then be all this to *me?* Did not the Son of God himself say that those should be his whom his father had given to him? And it *may* be that *I* have not been given to him—it may be, as my heart tells me it *is*, that the father has reserved me to himself.—I beseech you, William, do not mistake me—do not see a dark motive in these harmless words. My whole heart is spread out before you, or I should not have made the remark—I should not have wasted a moment on a subject where we are all equally and entirely ignorant.—Must not every man bear his own burthen?— must not every man drink his own cup? And if that cup was bit-

terness to the lips of tho Son of God, why should I in my pride
and presumption pretend that it is sweet to mine? [Why should
I be ashamed because in that fearful moment, when my very
existence trembles on the brink of annihilation—when the past
flashes its fearful light on the dark depths of futurity—when
every support sinks from beneath me, and the world fades and
disappears—in such a moment, is it not the voice of languishing,
exhausted nature that cries amidst our unavailing convulsions:
My God! My God! why hast thou forsaken me?—and shall I be
ashamed of that suffering, shall I look forward with dismay to
that moment which was not spared even to him who rolls together the heavens as a garment?

Nov. 21

She does not see—she does not feel that she is preparing a
poison which will destroy us both—and *I* drink with delight
from the cup which she gives me, though it is filled with my de-
struction. What does that tender look mean, which she often—
no, not *often*, but *sometimes* turns on me—the pure pleasure she
expresses at an unexpected burst of feeling—the interest in my
sufferings, which is stamped on her brow?

Yesterday, when I parted from her, she held out her hand
and said: "Good bye, my dear Werter."—*My dear* Werter!—
it was the first time she had ever called me *dear*, and I felt it in
every limb and articulation. I have repeated it to myself an hundred times since, and last night as I was going to bed alone and
talking to myself, I said: "Good night, *my dear* Werter," and
could not help laughing aloud at my own weakness.

Nov. 22

I must not pray that she may be mine, and yet I often think
of her as such—I must not pray that she be given to me, for she
is another's.—I am making myself merry with the bitterness
of my sorrows, and unless I stop, I shall give you a whole Litany
of antitheses.

Nov. 24

She is sensible to my sufferings. To-day a look she cast on me
went through my very heart. She was alone—I was silent—and
she looked at me steadfastly.—The splendour of beauty, the fire
of genius had faded and fled, but a higher charm dwelt in her
countenance—a deep interest, a tender compassion for my sorrows.—Why could not I have thrown myself at her feet?—Why

could I not have answered her look with a thousand kisses?—
She took refuge at her harpsichord and accompanied it with the
softest, deepest harmony. I never saw her lips so beautiful. They
seemed hardly to open, that they might receive the touching
tones which rose from the instrument and then echo them back
with added expression. I was overpowered and bowed my head
and solemnly vowed, "that I would never violate those lips, thus
guarded by celestial spirits"—And yet—I wish—O this happiness lies before me like an impassable gulph—and if I could but
plunge into it and expiate there my crimes—*crimes*?

Nov. 26

Sometimes I think my fate is solitary—that all other men are
comparatively happy—that there is no precedent for sufferings
like mine. Then, perhaps, I take up some poet of the elder times
and seem to read there the very history of my own heart. But,
yet, my sorrows are so deep!—And is it possible that other men
have had such sorrows, too?

Nov. 30

No, I shall never be myself again! I have received a solemn
warning to-day of the end of my sufferings and may hope and
doubt no more.

I had no appetite for dinner and therefore, at noon, went out
to take a walk by the river. The fields were deserted—a chilling
wind blew from the mountains—and a heavy, damp cloud rolled
through the valley. I saw at a distance a man in a green, tattered
cloak climbing among the rocks, seemingly in search of plants.
As I approached him, he looked round and discovered to me an
interesting face, whose prevalent expression was a melancholy
so gentle and subdued that it seemed only the index of feeling
and talent. Part of his black hair was rolled in curls and the rest
flowed loosely over his shoulders. As his dress proved him to be
one of the lower class of society, I thought he would not be offended if I should be curious about his employment, and therefore I asked him what he was looking for? "I am looking," said
he with a deep sigh, "for flowers." "But it is not the right
season," said I, smiling. "But there is a plenty of flowers," said
he coming close to me. "I have roses in my garden of two sorts,
and the later it is, the finer they are. My father gave me one of
them—they grow as wildly as weeds. I have been looking for
them these two days but I can't find them. There are yellow

flowers and blue and red, and the little centaury too, *that* has a beautiful flower—but I can find none of them." "And what would you do with them," said I, "if you had them?" A wild and convulsive smile distorted his countenance—"If you will not betray me," said he laying his finger on his lips, "I have promised a nosegay to my love." "That is right," said I. "O," he replied, "but she has a great many other things—she is rich, too.—" "And yet she loves your flowers," said I. "O," he went on, "she has jewels too, a crown."—"Who is she?"—"If the States General would but pay me," said he, "I should be quite another man. I used to be so happy once!—but now it is all over! I am *now*—" and a look of despair which he turned towards heaven told more than words. "*You*, too, were happy *once*," said I. "O, I wish I could be so again," he replied. "I felt so well!—so light-hearted! I was as happy as the fish in the stream."—"Henry!" cried an old woman coming towards us, "Henry! Why don't you come home. We have been looking for you every where—Come to dinner." "Is that your son?" said I advancing to her. "Yes," said she, "my poor child. God has laid a sore affliction upon me." "How long has he been in this way?" said I. "He has been as calm as he is now," she replied," about six months, and I thank Heaven he has—for one whole year he was chained in a mad house. Now he harms nobody, only he is always talking about kings and emperors. He used to be all gentleness and content and helped me to support myself by his fine hand-writing, but all at once he grew melancholy and then fell into a burning fever, then into madness and now he is what you see. If I should tell you, Sir—." I interrupted the torrent of her loquacity by asking when it was that he was so happy and contented. "Poor boy," said she with a melancholy smile, "he is always talking about that time—it was when he was in the mad-house and knew nothing." I was thunderstruck, gave her a piece of money —and left her wretched, indeed.

"*Then* you were happy," said I to myself, as I returned towards the town, "*then* you were as contented as a fish in his stream! Almighty God! is man then destined to know happiness only before his reason is developed or after it is lost? Poor wretch! —And yet how I envy that insensibility—that weakness and wandering, which to you was instead of happiness! You go forth in winter to gather flowers for your princess—and are grieved because you find none, but do not suspect the cause. And

I—*I* go forth without an object—without a hope, and return home as I went. You boast how different you should be if the States General would pay you! Happy wretch, who can assign so substantial a reason for his sorrows! You do not feel that your anguish is in your own desolate heart—in your own burning brain, and that all the emperors of the earth could not give you a moment's peace!"—

Perdition seize the wretch who can smile at the sick man who travels to distant springs only to increase his disease and add new poignancy to the pangs of death—who can despise the weakness and desolation of that heart, which to escape from its own reproaches or sorrows performs a pilgrimage to the Holy Sepulchre. Every thorn which pierces his feet on his rugged road, carries consolation to his bosom and with the wasting of every wearisome day his spirit is lightened of some thing of its burthen. And who shall be presumptuous enough to call this folly? O God, who beholdest my tears, is it not enough that man is so weak and imperfect, but must his brother wrest from him the little comfort—the little confidence he has in thee—*in thee*, his all-bountiful God? For what is confidence in a healing root or in the blessed vine—what is it but confidence in *thee*, who hast poured that health and consolation we hourly need on all that surrounds us.—My father, whom I know not, O, my father, who once didst fill me with light and life but now hidest thy face from me,—recall me to thyself, speak to my fainting spirit or I shall sink under the rebuke of thy silence!—And what *earthly* father's anger would rise against a son who should return even unbidden and fall on his neck and cry: "I have returned, my father, but be not angry that I have shortened the wanderings thou hadst appointed me. The world is, indeed, still the same—sorrow and toil have still their rewards and pleasures, but what can they profit *me*—me, who know no pleasure but in thy presence, and before whose face I would suffer or enjoy whatever awaits me!" And *thou*, O my *heavenly* father, wouldst *thou* drive such an one from thee?

Dec. 1

William, the happy wretch of whom I wrote to you was clerk to Charlotte's father, and a passion for her, which he cherished, concealed, and discovered, and for which he was dismissed from his employment, has driven him to madness. Learn now, from these few cold words, with what forebodings of despair I heard the story from Albert, who told it to me with as little emotion as you, perhaps, are now reading it.

Dec. 4

I beseech you—but it is all over with me—I can support it no longer! To-day I was sitting by her as she played several airs on her harpsichord, with such an expression!—Her youngest sister was dressing her doll in my lap.—The tears came into my eyes.—I leaned forward and my eye caught her wedding ring.— I wept like a child.—Suddenly she played a touching air which for a moment carried consolation to my heart, but soon brought with it a recollection of the hours when I first listened to it— of the dark succession of sufferings and disappointments which have followed and—I rose and walked up and down the room, but still the oppression continued to gather round my heart. "For Heaven's sake," said I turning suddenly towards her, "for Heaven's sake, stop!" She did, and looked with anxious astonishment in my face.—"Werter," said she with a smile that pierced my soul, "you must be very ill, since your favourite food offends you. Take a walk, I beseech you, and calm yourself."—I tore myself from her and—Almighty God! who beholdest my sufferings, *thou* wilt end them!—

Dec. 6

How her image haunts me! Waking or sleeping it fills all my thoughts. When I sink to rest, I find her dark eyes still fixed on me, still imprinted on the secret seat of vision in my brain, still—but I cannot describe it to you. If I shut my eyes, still they fasten on me, like a terrifying vision, and occupy every thought and faculty of my mind.

What then is man, the boasted child of heaven—man, whose strength faulters at the very instant it is most necessary he should exert it, and who, whether he is giddy with happiness or depressed by sorrow, must still return to a cold and comfortless existence, even at the moment when he most anxiously pants for immortality.

The Editor to the Reader

I wish our friend had left so full and connected an account of the last eventful days of his life that it would not be necessary for me to interrupt the remaining series of his letters with my own narration.

I have carefully collected his story from those persons who, from their situation, were best acquainted with it. It is simple, and all the accounts concur except in a very few unimportant particulars, which naturally appeared in a different light as they were considered with different feelings by persons unequally interested.

Nothing, therefore, remains but to repeat with scrupulous fidelity what has been so carefully collected, adding whatever remains of his own letters, without presuming to suppress the most inconsiderable fragment, especially since it is so difficult to decide on the secret and determining motive of even a single action of an extraordinary man.

Melancholy and ennui had taken deeper and deeper root in Werter's mind and wound themselves more and more closely about his heart, until at last they had obtained an unlimited empire over him. The harmony of his spirit was completely lost—a secret, burning impatience, which perpetually kept all his faculties in uneasy action upon each other, produced extravagance and absurdity of conduct and at last reduced him to a wearisome weakness, against which he contended even more strenuously than he had contended against all his former sufferings. The oppression at his heart impaired his mental faculties and the acuteness of his perceptions. He became an unpleasant companion, grew continually more unhappy, and, in proportion as he was more unhappy, became more unfit for society. This, at least, is the account given by Albert's friends. They say that Werter was incapable of comprehending the character of one who was so gentle and tranquil in the enjoyment of a happiness for which he had long sighed, or the efforts he made to secure its continuance—all this, they say, could not be understood by a man like Werter, who did but labour during the day to make for himself a night of sorrow and suffering. Albert, they say, had not changed so suddenly. He was still the same and still loved and honoured Werter as at the commencement of their acquaintance. His affection for

Charlotte was unlimited. He was proud of her, and anxious that her rare gifts should be known and acknowledged by the world. And was he to blame, if, after labouring to drive every form of suspicion from his mind, he still could not be contented in any way to divide his treasure with another? They acknowledge that Albert often left the room when Werter was with his wife, but not from coldness for his friend or aversion, but merely because he perceived that his presence was unwelcome.

Charlotte's father was taken sick and confined to his chamber, and he sent his carriage and brought her to him. It was a fine winter's day, and the first snow had just fallen and covered the country. The next morning Werter followed her, in order to accompany her home, if Albert should not come after her.

The pure air could not animate his troubled spirits—a heavy torpor oppressed his faculties—melancholy imaginations beset him round—and his mind turned only from one painful thought to another. As he lived in perpetual dissatisfaction with himself, the circumstances of those about him began to appear dark and troubled to him. He imagined he had interrupted the confidence which had subsisted between Albert and his wife, and his self-reproach on this account was mingled with a secret bitterness towards his friend.

As he went on, he revolved all these circumstances in his mind. "Yes," said he to himself with stifled passion, "this, forsooth, is the deep confidence of friendship, the tender interest of affection—this is the composure of assured fidelity. O no! it is satiety, it is indifference! Does he not find more satisfaction in the fulness of his business than in the society of his affectionate and devoted wife? Is he sensible of his happiness? Can he value her, as she ought to be valued?—He has obtained the prize—that is it—he has obtained the prize!—Well, I know that as I know any thing else—and I thought I should have become accustomed to it, as I am accustomed to other things—but it will drive me to despair—it will destroy me! And does his regard for me still continue? Does he not already see an intrusion on his prerogative in my dependence on Charlotte—and are not my devoted attentions to her a silent reproach to him? O, I know very well —I feel it—he regards me with an alter'd eye—my presence disturbs him.—"

He often stopped in his giddy course—often stood still and silent—and seemed resolved not to go on—but still he went forward again, and in the midst of his thoughts and exclamations reached the door of the hunting-lodge, as it were against his will.

He went in and inquired for the Steward and Charlotte. The house seemed in some confusion. The eldest boy told him that a dreadful thing had happened at Walheim—that a peasant had been killed! It made no impression on him. He went into the parlour and found Charlotte in earnest conversation with her father, who, notwithstanding his illness, seemed determined to go out and inquire into the circumstances of the case on the spot where they happened. The perpetrator was not yet discovered—the deceased was found before his own door in the morning—suspicions were entertained, as the victim was the servant of a widow, who had before had another servant, whom she had dismissed for ill-conduct.

The instant Werter heard this, he started up and left the house. "What!" said he, "is it possible? I must go over there—I cannot have a moment's peace!—" He hurried to Walheim, with every recollection fresh in his memory and with hardly a doubt that the man who had done the deed was the one of whom he had spoken so often and for whom he had so much regard.

As he passed the lime-trees on his way to the inn where they had laid out the body, he shuddered at the recollections they revived. That porch around which the village children had so often held their pastime was now foul with blood—the kindest and most affectionate of human feelings, that once dwelt there, had been changed to violence and murder—the trees were stripped of their foliage and white with frost—and through the intervals between the naked and leafless shrubbery which lined the humble church-yard wall his eye caught a glimpse of the grave-stones half covered with snow.

As he approached the inn, before which the whole village was assembled, a sudden cry arose, and, at a distance, he saw a number of armed men approaching, and some one cried out, they were bringing the culprit. Werter saw him, and his last doubt vanished, for it was indeed the young man who had been so affectionately attached to the widow. "Miserable wretch," said Werter springing towards him, "what have you done?" The young man looked at him calmly—was silent a moment—and then replied with resolute composure—"No man shall have her and she shall have no man." They carried him into the inn and Werter hurried away.

By this violent shock all his faculties and feelings were thrown into commotion and conflict. He was started at once from his melancholy and indifference—became deeply interested in the young man's fate—and was moved with an irresistible desire to save him. He saw that his condition was most wretched —he considered him even as an offender so comparatively guilt- less—he, in short, so completely identified himself with the suf- ferer that he began to imagine he could convince others of his in- nocence. He already desired to become his advocate—the eloquent appeal he intended to make already trembled on his lips—he turned hastily towards the hunting-lodge and on his way could not refrain from repeating aloud what he intended to urge upon the Steward.

When he entered the parlour he found Albert there. This, for a moment, disconcerted him, but he soon returned to his original in- tention, and laid his feelings and wishes before the Steward. The Steward shook his head, and, notwithstanding Werter, in a tumult of eloquence and earnestness and passion, urged every thing that could be urged, still, as will easily be believed, the Steward was inflexible. Nay more, he interrupted him, replied to him with vehemence, and reproached him with protecting a murderer. He told him that, in this way, all justice would be over- thrown, and all personal security destroyed—and showed him that he could not interfere in such a matter without assuming a very dangerous responsibility—and that, in fact, every thing must go on with regularity and in the prescribed course.

Werter did not yet despair. He asked the Steward to connive at any measures which might be taken to assist the young man's escape. This the Steward promptly and distinctly refused. Albert, who now for the first time joined the conversation, went over to the Steward's side. Werter was silenced and returned home full of grief and despair, after the Steward had repeatedly said to him: "No, he is not to escape!"

From a memorandum found among his papers, which was probably written on the day these incidents happened, we can easily see how deep an impression these words made upon him.

"Poor wretch, you are not to escape! And *we*, too, I see plainly enough, *we* are not to escape."

What Albert had said on the case of the young man, at the Steward's, had offended Werter deeply. He imagined he dis- covered in it the proofs of a secret ill-will to himself, and though on calmer reflection it seemed at least probable they might be right, yet the confession of his error and the surrender of his opinion seemed to him like a renunciation of all he had or hoped.

We have found among his papers a fragment which will, perhaps, explain all his feelings towards Albert.

"What matters it that I say to myself again and again, he is a high-minded, worthy man—when it is such an outrage to my feelings. I must be wrong."

As the evening was fine and the weather had become more mild, Charlotte and Albert walked home. As they passed along, Charlotte looked about from one side to the other as if she missed Werter's customary attendance. Albert began to speak of him— blamed his extravagancies but did justice to his feelings. He lamented his unfortunate attachment and wished for Werter's own sake that he might be induced to leave them. "I wish it for *our* sake also," said he, "and I wish too," he went on, "that it were possible for you to give another character to his attentions and diminish the frequency of his visits. The world is censorious, and I know they are already beginning to be the subject of re- mark." Charlotte was silent and Albert seemed to be touched by it.

At least, from that time, he never mentioned Werter to her, and if she mentioned him, he suffered the conversation to sub- side or gave it another direction.

Werter's unvailing attempt to save the peasant was the last fitful flash of an expiring flame. He now relapsed into a deeper melancholy and listlessness, except that he was once suddenly aroused when he heard he should probably be cited as a witness against the young man, who now obstinately denied his guilt.

All the untoward accidents which had occurred to him in the course of his active life—all the circumstances of his insult while he was with the ambassador—all his disappointments and all his mortifications rose and passed and repassed before his memory. He went on to persuade himself from a consideration of them all that he was justified in his listlessness and inactivity—that he was cut off from all hope and incapable of entering into the com- mon business of life, until at last, by his feelings, his melancholy, and his passion for the most lovely and beloved of women, whose peace he had impaired, he was continually carried forward in the fruitless struggle and confusion of his faculties towards a melancholy end.

A few letters, which we will now insert, furnish the strong- est proof of his doubts, of his restless impatience, his troubled feelings, and weariness of life.

"My dear William, I am in the condition of those miserable wretches who are supposed to have been possessed of unclean spirits. The malady attacks me at intervals. It is not sorrow—it is not passion—it is a deep and secret frenzy which oppresses and suffocates me—and drives me forth to wander at night amidst the dark and solemn scenery which this unfriendly season exhibits.

"Last evening I was driven out by these feelings. All the streams, I understood, had been raised by a sudden inundation and had overflown their banks, so that from Walheim to this place my favourite valley was completely under water. I hastened there, though it was past XI o'clk. It was a fearful sight, as I stood on a projecting rock and saw by the imperfect light of the moon the waves rolling over fields and meadows and bushes, and the whole valley as far as the eye could reach one waste of waters tossed and beaten by the storm. And when the moon burst out and seemed to sleep on the dark clouds, and the river as it heaved and roared in fearful majesty beneath me grew bright with the dazzling reflection—I drew near to the precipice and stretched forth my arms and shuddered and wished and lost myself in the happy thought of burying there all my sorrows and all my sufferings—of mingling and heaving with its restless and turbulent waves. O, why were my feet rooted to the earth? Why could I not then have ended my misery? My hour has not yet come—I feel it has not! *But* for this, my dear William, O, how gladly would I have thrown off the burthen of mortality—How gladly would I have risen on the tempest that rends the clouds and torments and tosses the waves.—And may I not one day escape from my prison?—May I not one day enjoy this happiness?

"I looked anxiously for a spot, where I had sat with Charlotte under a willow after a weary walk—that, too, was overflown, and I could hardly distinguish even the willow. My mind then turned to the meadow and grounds by the hunting-lodge.—'Perhaps,' thought I, 'all these and even the arbour are laid waste by the furious flood'—and with this thought a ray of the past flashed upon me, as a dream of his home and his fields and his occupations visits the convicted malefactor.—I hesitated—but I do not reproach myself for it, for I dare to die—I should, if—but now, I am still here, like a decrepit old woman who gleans her wood from the hedges and begs her bread from door to door, merely to prolong for one poor moment a wretched and unprofitable existence."

Dec. 14

"What can it mean? Is not my love for her pure and hallowed —is it not the love of a brother? Have I ever felt a guilty wish in my heart?—I will not resort to protestations.—And, yet such dreams!—O, how deeply were they read in human nature, who ascribed them to supernatural agency! Last night—I tremble as I write it—last night, I held her in my arms, I pressed her to my bosom, I covered her lips with burning kisses.—My eyes swam with the giddy frenzy they caught from her's—! O God! is the delight I still feel in recalling these transports a crime?—Charlotte! Charlotte! my fate is decided! My senses wander!—for a week I have lost the power of recollection.—My eyes are full of tears—I am equally happy and equally wretched wherever I am—I ask for nothing—I hope for nothing—it is better for me to go."

The resolution to leave the world had now, from the force of such circumstances, been gaining yet greater strength in Werter's mind. Since his return to Charlotte it had been continually before him, as his final hope and refuge, but he had determined not to take such a step rashly or with precipitation but upon the deepest conviction and with the most deliberate firmness.

His secret doubts and struggles may be discovered from a few lines that were found among his papers without any date and seem to have been the commencement of a letter to Albert.

"Her present situation, her future prospects, and her interest in mine force the last tears from my burning brain.

"It is only to lift the curtain and enter within the scene! Why, then, do I hesitate and tremble? Is it because it is impossible to know what lies on the other side and because there is no return? It is in our very nature to exaggerate those dangers we do not comprehend."

By degrees these melancholy thoughts became more familiar and dear to him, and the following letter to his friend will show the deliberate calmness of his final purpose.

Dec. 20

"I thank you, my dear William, for the meaning your affection has given to my words. Yes, you are right:—'It is better for me to go'—but I do not altogether like your plan of returning to your neighborhood. At any rate, I should like to make a little excursion first, especially as we have a prospect of the continuance of the frost and good roads. I am not insensible to your kindness in proposing to come for me, but I must beg you to postpone it for a fortnight and at any rate not to come until you have received another letter from me. Nothing should be done prematurely, and a fortnight may make great changes. Ask my mother to pray for her child and to forgive all the anxiety and sorrow I have occasioned her. I have always been destined to add burthens to those whose burthens I ought to have borne. Farewell, dearest William, may Heaven's choicest blessings rest upon you—Farewell!"

What was passing at this time in Charlotte's mind, what were her feelings towards her husband and towards her unfortunate friend, we shall hardly attempt to describe, though we feel assured that a knowledge of her character will lead every one to a just estimate of her situation, and that the delicacy of a female heart, in particular, cannot choose but understand the circumstances in which she was placed and sympathize with the conflict of her feelings.

This, however, is certain. She had resolved to exert herself to the utmost to persuade Werter to leave them for a time, and if she hesitated, it was only from the natural reluctance of a kind disposition to give pain, for she knew how much it would cost Werter—how nearly, indeed, it would be impossible. This, however, at last, only tended to fortify her resolution. She was entirely silent on the subject to her husband as she had always been, and she had besides determined to show him by the firmness of her conduct that her affection was no less deep than his own.

On the evening of the day when Werter wrote the preceding letter to his friend (it was the Sunday before Christmas) he went to see Charlotte and found her alone. She was busy in preparing a little exhibition for the children on Christmas eve. He remarked on children's feelings at such times—at the moment when the unexpected opening of the door and discovery of the illuminated trees, the confectionary and fruit seems to place them at once in the enjoyment of paradise. "And you," said Charlotte concealing her feelings under an affectionate smile, "*you*, too, shall have a present and see the illumination, if you behave well." "And what *is* behaving well?" he replied. "What *ought* I to be, dearest Charlotte? what *can* I be?" "Thursday evening," said she, "is Christmas eve, and the children will be here and my father, and each will have his present, and *you,* too, if you come then—and not before." Werter was thunderstruck. "I beseech you," said she, "for it has come to this—I beseech you for the sake of my peace—we cannot, *must* not go on in this way!"—Charlotte saw the fearful struggle which these words had excited and endeavoured by a variety of inquiries to divert his thought, but it was all in vain. "No, Charlotte," said he, interrupting her, "no, I will never see you again." "And why not?" she replied. "You *can* see us again, Werter, and you *must,* only not so frequently. Oh, why were you formed with that impatience, with that ungoverned impetuosity, which carries extravagance into all you undertake. I beseech you," she added taking his hand, "be more rational. Do not your feelings, your acquirements, your talents open to you numberless sources of enjoyment? Be a man, then, and cast off an unhappy passion for one who can offer you only her pity." He started and looked at her almost in anger. She still held his hand—"Give me but a single moment of calm attention," said she. "Do you not feel that you are deceiving yourself, that you are voluntarily rushing to your own ruin? And why should it be for *me,* Werter, and none *but me,* who am another's? I fear, Werter, I fear, that it is only the impossibility of attaining the object, which has placed such a charm upon it." He withdrew his hand from her's and looked at her with a fixed and angry gaze. "Shrewd," said he, "very shrewd! Perhaps Albert suggested the remark. Politick, quite politick!" "It is a remark," she replied, "which is sufficiently obvious to be made by any body. And is there not *one* else in the world, who can satisfy all the wishes of your heart? Get the mastery of yourself! Look abroad in the world for her, and my life for it, you shall not look in vain. The solitude in which you have lately lived has alarmed me for *you* and for ourselves.— Get the mastery of yourself! You will, you *must* try the effect of a journey. Look, too, for an object worthy of your affections and, when you have found her, return and enjoy with us all the happiness that intimacy and friendship can give." "Your remarks," said he, with an unnatural smile, "ought to be published for the common benefit of philosophy. My dear Charlotte, give me but a little more peace, and all will be well." "Yes, Werter, on condition you do not come again, until Christmas eve." He was about to reply, when Albert came in. Their salutation was cold and formal, and then with obvious embarassment they walked up and down the room together. Werter began some common-place remarks but soon discontinued them. Albert made the same attempt with the same success, and then asked his wife about some business he had left with her. She told him she had not attended to it, and he replied in a few words, which to Werter seemed cold and even unkind. He attempted to go, but could not. His agitation and embarassment continued to increase and he lingered until VIII o'clk, when the servant came to set the supper-table and he took his hat to go. Albert asked him to stay, but Werter, who considered it an unmeaning formality, thanked him coldly and went away.

He returned home, took the candle from his servant, and went alone to his chamber—wept aloud—talked to himself—walked hastily about the room—and at last, without undressing, threw himself on his bed, where his servant found him at XI o'clk, when he went to ask him whether he should pull off his boots. Werter told him he might, and then directed him not to interrupt him in the morning until he called him.

Early on Monday morning the twenty first of December he began the following letter to Charlotte, which was found sealed on his table after his death and delivered to Charlotte. I shall insert it in fragments, explaining each by an account of the circumstances under which it was written.

"Yes, Charlotte, it is determined!—*I will die!*—and I write it to you, not only without any romantick extravagance, but with unmoved calmness on the morning of the day in which I shall see you for the last time. When you read this, dearest, the cold grave will already have covered the lifeless remains of that restless, wretched man, who, to the last moment of his life, knew no happiness other than that he found with you.—I have passed a dreadful night, but it has been profitable to me, for it has determined and settled my resolution—*I will die!*—When I tore myself from you yesterday my senses were in the wildest disorder—my heart was closed and cold.—I reached my chamber with difficulty and fell on my kness, and, for the last time, my God vouchsafed me the bitter consolation of tears. A thousand designs, a thousand prospects rose in rapid succession to my mind—and when they had all subsided, the first, the last, the final determination rested firmly there—*I will die!*—I went to bed, and in the morning, in the calmness of my waking thoughts, *there* it still stood in solitary firmness—*I will die!* It is not

despair, Charlotte—it is the assurance I feel that I shall thus
expiate my offenses and offer myself up for you. Yes, Charlotte
—why should I attempt to conceal it?—One of us three must
die! and *I* will be the voluntary victim.—O, my dear Charlotete,
the thought of murdering your husband—you—myself has often
passed through my distracted mind.—Let it, therefore, be determined!—

"When you go up towards the mountain in a summer's evening, then remember *me*, Charlotte, who have so often climbed
its precipices—then look back towards the churchyard, towards
my grave, and watch the tall grass that waves over me, gilded
by the last rays of the setting sun.—I was calm when I began,
but now—*now* that the prospect rises so distinctly before me, I
weep like a child."

At about X o'clk Werter called his servant and told him, as
if he were going on a journey, to collect his clothes and prepare them to be packed—to call in his bills—to bring home
the books he had lent—and to give a two months' stipend to some
poor people, who had been accustomed to receive a weekly allowance from him.

He suffered his breakfast to be brought to him in his room
and then rode over to the Steward's, but did not find him at home.
He walked up and down the garden in a melancholy mood, and
seemed voluntarily to resign himself to the bitter recollections
it awakened.

The children, however, did not suffer him to remain long un-
disturbed. They followed him, jumped about him, and told him,
that, after tomorrow and tomorrow and one day more, they
should keep Christmas eve at Charlotte's, and described to him
all the wonders which their little imaginations had promised
them. "To-morrow," he repeated, "and to-morrow, and one day
more!"—and kissed them tenderly and was on the point of leav-
ing them, when the youngest came up to him and whispered in
his ear: 'that his elder brothers had prepared very fine new-
year's wishes and very long ones besides—one for papa—one for
Charlotte and Albert, and one for Mr. Werter, too—which they
were going to present early on new-year's morning.' Werter was
completely unmanned by this unexpected simplicity. He gave
something to each of them—mounted horse—left his respects
for the Steward—and rode away with his eyes full of tears.

He reached home at about five o'clk and told the maid to take care of his fire and keep it burning during the evening.—He ordered his servant to pack his books at the bottom of his trunk and his clothes at the top, and about this time seems to have continued the letter to Charlotte.

"You do not expect me—you think I shall obey you and shall not see you again before Christmas-eve.—O, Charlotte, to-day or never! On Christmas eve you will hold this paper in your trembling hand and wet it with your tears. I will—*I must*— O, how tranquil I have been, since I ceased to doubt!"

Charlotte, in the mean time, had found herself in a very difficult situation. From her last conversation with Werter, she had learned how much it would cost her to lose him and how difficult it would be for him to tear himself away.

She had incidentally said before Albert that Werter would not be there again before Christmas-eve, and Albert had gone to transact some business with a publick agent in a neighboring town, which would detain him from home all night.

She was alone—none even of the children were with her and she gave herself up to her own reflections, which still dwelt on her peculiar situation. She found herself united to one of whose affection and confidence she felt assured, and to whom she was sincerely devoted—one whose peace and happiness heaven had placed in her hands as a sacred trust which it should be a wife's privilege and pleasure to watch and preserve—one who, she felt, would be every thing to herself and to the children. On the other hand, Werter had become extremely dear to her. The first moment of their acquaintance, in which they felt that they were congenial spirits—their subsequent intimacy and the various interesting situations in which they had been placed together— every thing had conspired to make an impression on her heart which could never be effaced. She had been accustomed to share all her thoughts and feelings with him, and his absence threatened to leave an aching void in her bosom which could never again be filled. O, she thought if she could at this moment have changed him to a brother—if she could have married him to a friend, and restored his intimacy with Albert—she *thought* she should have been happy. She ran through the circle of her friends, but still there was some fault in each—and after all, she found not one to whom she would willingly have surrendered him.

From all these reflections, she first began to see indistinctly that it was the unacknowledged wish of her heart to keep him still exclusively her own, but she immediately determined that she could not do it. Her pure spirits, which once had been so gay and had so easily cast aside the burthen of sorrow, gradually fell as this prospect of happiness closed upon her. Her heart sunk within her and a dark cloud seemed to settle around her.

It was now half past six o'clk, and she heard Werter coming up the stairs and immediately recognized his step and voice, as he asked for her. Her heart beat violently—and it is not too much to say, it was the *first* time it had ever beat at his approach. She would gladly have denied herself to him—and as soon as he entered the room, she said with a kind of hurried and embarassed earnestness, "You have not kept your word."—"I did not promise," he replied. "You might, at least, have paid more regard to my request," she answered, "as it was made for both our sakes."

She hardly knew what she said and was equally ignorant what she was doing when she sent out for some friends that she might not be alone with Werter. She turned over several books he had brought her, asked about some others—and wished sometimes that her friends would come and sometimes that they might be prevented. At last the servant returned with an apology—that they were both engaged.

She then thought she would direct her maid to sit with her work in the next room, but changed her mind. Werter walked up and down the room. She went to her instrument and played a minuet, but still every thing went wrong. At last she summoned all her resolution and sat quietly down by Werter who occupied his accustomed place on the sofa.

"Have you nothing to read to me?" said she. No, he had nothing. "Then look in my drawer and you will find your translation of some passages of Ossian. I have not yet read it, for I have been hoping you would read it to me, but lately you have not been good for much." He smiled and went for the papers. His hand trembled as he took them, and the moment he opened them his eyes were filled with tears. He sat down and read:

"Alone on the sea-beat-rock, my daughter was heard to complain. Frequent and loud were her cries; nor could her father relieve her. All night I stood on the shore. I saw her by the faint beam of the moon. All night I heard her cries. Loud was the wind and the rain beat hard on the side of the mountain. Before morning appeared, her voice was weak. It died away like the evening breeze among the grass of the rock. Spent with grief she expired and left thee, Armina, alone. Gone is my strength in the war and fallen my pride among women. When the storms of the mountain come; when the North lifts the waves on high; I sit by the sounding shore and look on the fatal rock. Often by the setting moon I see the ghosts of my children. Half viewless, they walk in mournful conference together."

[Here Ticknor has omitted several pages of Ossian. Ed.]

A flood of tears, which burst from Charlotte's eyes and relieved the oppression at her heart, interrupted Werter's reading. He threw down the paper, seized her hand, and wept bitterly. Charlotte leaned on the other and hid her face in her handkerchief. It was a fearful trial for both of them. They felt that it was but a reflection of their own sorrows—they felt it in common —they felt it at the same moment—and their tears had flowed and mingled together. The lips and eyes of Werter were fastened on Charlotte's hand. She trembled and endeavored to move away from him, but sorrow and sympathy prevented her. At last she partly recovered herself, and in a broken voice, but one which fell on him like a voice from heaven, she begged him to go on. He hesitated—his heart was full almost to bursting—he took up the papers and read in a faultering accent:—

"Why dost thou awake, O gale! It seems to say: 'I am covered with the drops of heaven. The time of my fading is near, and the blast that shall scatter my leaves. To-morrow shall the traveller come—he who saw me in my beauty shall come—his eyes will search the field, but they will not find me.' "

The whole force of this passage fell on his heart. In the fulness of his despair, he threw himself at her feet, seized her hands and pressed them against his eyes and his forehead and thus gave her a dark intimation of his horrible purpose. Her reason wandered.—She pressed his hand, pressed it against her bosom— and in the bitterness of her anguish bent forward until her burning cheek met his. The world disappeared and was forgotten. He caught her in his arms, pressed her to his bosom, and covered her trembling, hesitating lips with frantick kisses. "Werter," she cried in a faultering voice, turning away from him—"Werter!" she repeated, feebly endeavoring to disengage herself.—"Werter!" at last she cried in the firm tone of recollected reason, and he was awed, released her from his arms, and fell powerless at her feet. She rose and in the anguish of her thoughts, trembling between tenderness and resentment, cried: "It is the last time,

Werter, you shall never see me again!" and then casting a look of unmingled affection upon him, passed into the adjoining room and bolted the door. Werter stretched out his arms towards her, but did not presume to prevent her. He remained on the floor with his head resting on the sofa more than half an hour, until he was aroused by a noise. It was the maid who had come to lay the table. He walked up and down the room until he found himself alone, then went to the door and said in a low tone: "Charlotte, Charlotte—only one word, one farewell!" She made no reply. He waited—and prayed—and waited again—then tore himself away and cried: "Farewell, Charlotte! Farewell forever!"

He came to the city-gate. The watchman knew him and suffered him to pass unmolested. It was now about eleven o'clk, and it stormed both rain and snow. His servant observed that he was without his hat but did not venture to make any remark upon it, and when he undressed his master he observed that his clothes were wet through. His hat was afterwards found on a high, projecting rock, which overlooks the valley, and it is inconceivable how he could have climbed there in a night so dark and stormy without being precipitated down the cliffs below.

He went to bed and slept until late in the morning. His servant found him writing, when he was called to bring him his coffee. It was the continuation of his letter to Charlotte.—

"For the last time, then—for the last time, I have awaked— I shall never again behold the sun—it is hidden by this dark and melancholy storm.—But it is fit that Nature should thus mourn, for her child, her friend, her favourite draws near to the grave. Charlotte, when I tell you this is *my last day*, I feel a sensation which has no precedent or parallell, but which is most like the doubt and darkness of a dream.. *The last!* The phrase has no meaning in my mind. Do I not stand here to-day in the independence of my strength? And to-morrow I shall sleep in the cold and silent grave. *To die? What is it?* We do but dream when we talk of death. I have stood by many a death-bed, but the limits of human reason are so narrow that it cannot reach back beyond the commencement or forward beyond the conclusion of our present existence. *Now* I am still my own—still *thine*, dearest Charlotte, *thine!* and, in an instant, we are torn asunder—separated—perhaps forever? No, Charlotte, no. How is it possible, that *I* should be annihilated—that *you* should be annihilated, for do we not *exist?* Annihilation? What is it?—a word—a mere sound, that carries no meaning to my heart! Dead, Charlotte? Constrained within the dark and narrow house!—I had a friend once, who was every thing to the helplessness of my childhood. She died and I followed her bier—I stood by the grave and saw the coffin descend into the earth and heard the creaking of the cords. The first shovelfull of earth was thrown in, and it returned a hollow sound, which grew fainter and more dull until it was at last entirely covered.—I threw myself on the grave—my heart was rent with anguish—and yet I knew not the loss I had suffered or the sorrows that awaited me. To die! The grave! I comprehend it not!

"O forgive me! forgive me! Yesterday! It should have been the last day of my life. Angel of light! for the first time, I felt an intimate and undoubting assurance of my happiness! for the first time I knew that you loved me, that you loved me! The holy flame which they caught from your lips still burns on mine, and fills my heart with new warmth and life. Forgive me! Forgive me!

"O, I knew that you loved me—I knew it by your first glance —I knew it the first time you pressed my hand. And yet, when you were away or when Albert sat at your side, my confidence again subsided into feverish doubts.

"Do you remember the flower you sent me, when in that wearisome crowd you could not get an opportunity to speak to me or to give me your hand? O, I knelt before that flower half the night, for it was the witness and pledge of your affection. But, alas! such impressions pass away, as the recollection of the mercy of God gradually fades even from the memory of faith, though it had been inscribed there in burning characters by the very hand of heaven. *These* all fade and disappear, but not eternity can efface the transports which I yesterday drew from your lips and which still live and glow within me. She loves me! These arms have embraced her! These lips have trembled on her's! She is mine! You are mine, Charlotte, mine forever!

"And what matters it that Albert is your husband? It is but in this world—and, in this world, is it not a crime for me to love you? is it not a crime that I should have the power of tearing you from a husband's arms? A crime? Well, I shall punish myself for it. I have enjoyed the very luxury of guilt and it has filled my heart with the balsam and buoyancy of life. From this moment you are mine, Charlotte, you are mine! I go before you, indeed, to my father and to your father, and I will cry to him and he will comfort me until you come, and then I shall fly to meet you—then I shall claim you, and before the face of the ever-lasting God we shall meet and dwell forever.

"I do not dream—I do not rave. As I approach the tomb, the prospect grows more bright and distinct. I feel more assured that we shall meet again and meet your mother—that I shall see her and know her and pour out my whole heart before her."

At about XI o'clk Werter asked his servant if Albert had returned. The servant told him he had, for he had seen his horse put up. Werter then sent him with the following unsealed billet:

"Will you have the goodness to lend me your pistols for a journey I intend to take? Farewell."

Charlotte had passed a troubled and miserable night. What she dreaded had come to pass and come to pass, too, in a way which she had neither feared nor fancied to be possible. Her blood, which had formerly flowed with such even tranquillity, was thrown into a feverish tumult, and her light heart was pierced with a thousand bitter reflections. Was it the flame she had caught from Werter's embrace that wrought thus within her bosom? Was it a secret reproach for her own weakness? Was it a distressing comparison of her present situation with the past days of unreproved innocence and careless self-confidence? How should she meet her husband? How should she explain to him a scene which she longed to confess and yet whose confession would cost her so much? They had for a long time observed a conventional silence, and ought she to be the first to break it, and at the most unpropitious moment possible make a discovery so unexpected and extraordinary? She feared, indeed, that the mere fact of Werter's visit would produce an unpleasant impression on his mind—how much more, then, its strange catastrophe? Had she a right to hope that her husband would see her conduct exactly as he ought to see it, and receive her confession without reproach? And could she dare to wish that he might read all the thoughts of her heart? And then, on the other hand, how could she practise any concealment towards one before whom she had always stood in transparent simplicity and sincerity, and from whom she never had hidden and never could hope to hide a single feeling of her heart. Either alternative was distressing and the hesitation between them yet more so. Her thoughts, too, still returned to Werter, who was now lost to her—whom it seemed impossible for her to give up—and yet alas! whom she *must* herself cast off and whom when she had lost, she had lost every thing.

The difficulty between Albert and Werter about herself, though she did not clearly understand it, now pressed heavily upon her. It seemed indeed strange that two men of such strong understandings and such high worth should, from a secret distrust of each other, first grow silent and reserved and then become jealous of their mutual rights and injuries, until, at last, their relations and differences had become so much involved and perplexed that it was impossible to disentangle the knot at the critical moment when every thing depended on it. Had a fortunate expression of confidence once brought them near to each other—had affection and kindness revived, and had their hearts been again opened and trusted to each other, perhaps Werter might yet have been saved.

A singular circumstance now came into operation. Werter, as we have seen from his letters, had never made any secret of his earnest desire to leave the world. Albert had often rebuked him for it, and it had sometimes been the subject of conversation between Charlotte and her husband. But Albert had such an incredulous abhorrence of suicide that he sometimes hinted with a sort of contempt not at all natural to him that he was always disposed to doubt the seriousness of such determinations, and indulged himself in occasional witticisms upon them until at last Charlotte partly joined in his incredulity. On one side, therefore, this doubt calmed her apprehensions, whenever the dreadful vision rose to her thoughts, and on the other she was hindered by it from imparting to her husband the fears that still oppressed her.

Albert returned and Charlotte met him with a hurried and embarassed earnestness. He was dispirited—had not finished his business and had found the agent mean and impracticable. He was besides fatigued by his ride in the storm.

He asked what had happened during his absence, and she replied with suspicious promptness that Werter had been there the evening before. He then inquired whether any letters had come for him, and was told that there were several letters and packets in his room. He went there and Charlotte remained alone. The presence of a husband whom she loved and honoured so much made a new impression on her heart. The recollection of his generous attachment and high worth increased her agitation. She felt a secret desire to follow him and took up her work and went into his room, as she had often been accustomed to do. He was employed in opening and reading his letters, some of which seemed to contain unpleasant intelligence. She asked him a few questions, which he answered abruptly and sat down at his table to write.

They continued in this irksome situation about an hour, during which Charlotte's spirits every moment fell lower and lower. She felt how difficult it would be for her to explain her feelings to her husband, even in a moment of gaiety and kindness, and the thought of it added to her agitation and distress which were yet farther increased by her endeavours to restrain and conceal her tears.

The arrival of Werter's servant completed her misery. He gave the note to Albert, who carelessly passed it to his wife saying: "Give him the pistols"—and then turning to the servant added: "I wish him a pleasant journey."—Charlotte was thunderstruck—endeavoured in vain to get up, and seemed to lose all consciousness of what she was doing. At last she went slowly towards the wall, took down the pistols, wiped off the dust, trembled, hesitated, and, if a glance from Albert had not admonished her, would have lingered yet longer. She gave the dreadful weapons to the servant without being able to utter a syllable and as soon as he was gone, collected her work together and went to her chamber overwhelmed with despair. Her heart foreboded all the horrors that awaited her. At intervals she was on the point of returning and throwing herself at the feet of her husband and telling him every thing—the history of the last evening, all her guilt and all her fears. But, on reflection, she found it would be followed by no good consequences—and least of all could she hope to persuade him to go to Werter. The table, at last, was laid and a kind friend, who called but for a moment and yet stayed the afternoon, made their dinner more supportable.

The servant returned with the pistols to Werter, who received them with transports when he knew that Charlotte had given them to him. He then ordered some bread and wine, told his servant to go to dinner, and sat down to continue his letter.

"They have passed through your hands, and *you* wiped the

dust from them. I kissed them a thousand times, for you had touched them.—And thou, Almighty father, thou hast smiled on my purpose—and *you*, Charlotte, from *your* hands I have received the weapon—those hands from which I have so often prayed to receive my death, and through which alas! it has now reached me. O, how I have questioned my servant! You trembled when you gave them to him, but you did not send me one farewell! alas! alas! you did not send me one farewell!—Is it right thus to shut up your heart against me for that very moment which unites me to you forever? Charlotte, ages cannot impair that impression! and I feel in my heart that you cannot hate one who loves you so truly for your own sake."

After dinner, he ordered his servant to finish packing his things, tore up a great many papers, and then went out and discharged some trifling debts. He returned and soon afterwards, notwithstanding the storm, went to the Marquis's garden—walked about the fields and came home again just before dark.

"William, I have seen the woods and fields and skies for the last time! Farewell, also, to thee! Farewell! Dearest mother forgive me!—Comfort her, William! God bless you! Farewell! We shall meet again—and in a happier world.

"I have ill-requited your kindness, Albert, and you forgive me for it. I have disturbed the peace of your home—I have interrupted your domestick confidence.—Farewell! I shall interrupt it no longer. Would to God your happiness could be restored by my death. Albert! Albert! as you hope for the favour of heaven, make her happy."

He was occupied during the evening with his papers—tore up a great many and burnt them and sealed up others and directed them to William. They consisted of loose memoranda and detached thoughts, several of which I have seen. At X o'clk he directed his fire to be rebuilt and sent for some wine—and then dismissed his servant for the night, whose chamber was in a remote part of the house and who slept in his clothes in order to be quickly ready in the morning, as his master had told him that he had ordered the horses to be at the door before VI o'clk.

Past eleven o'clk.

"All is silent around me, and all is tranquil within me. I thank thee, O Almighty father! that in my last moments thou hast vouchsafed me such warmth and vigour.

"From my window, dearest Charlotte, I can see, still see at intervals, through the dark and driving clouds, a few of the stars of the everlasting firmament. No! you shall not fall—the arm of the Almighty supports both you and me. I can distinguish the beam of Libra—my chosen constellation.—When I used to come away from your door at the close of the evening, it stood directly opposite to me. How often have I gazed at it with transport! How often have I stretched forth my hands towards it as the hallowed witness and monument of my happiness! And now—! O Charlotte, what is there that does not remind me of you? Do you not live in every thing that surrounds me, and have I not, like a child, hoarded every trifle which has been consecrated by your touch?

"Your profile, which was so dear to me, I return to you, Charlotte, and beseech you to honour and cherish it. I have impressed thousands and thousands of kisses upon it. I have bowed down before it thousands of times as I entered and left my chamber.

"I have written to your father and asked him to protect my remains. In the field by the church-yard are two lime-trees—it is there I wish to rest. He can and will do this for the sake of his friend. Join with me in my request.—But I would not disturb those pious Christians who might shudder at the thought of resting by a wretch like me—Ah! then, let me be buried by the common way-side or in the solitude of the valley, that the Priest and the Levite may thank their God and pass by on the other side, while the Samaritan gives a tear to my fate.

"The time draws near. Charlotte, I do not tremble as I take the cold and horrible cup from which I am to drink the anguish of death—for it is you who offer it to me and I cannot hesitate. Every wish, every hope of my life—*every* one is thus fulfilled, and I hasten through the iron gates of the grave.

"Would to God it could be granted me to die for *you*, Charlotte—to offer myself up for *your* sake! I should die in peace— I should die happy, if I could restore peace and happiness to you. But alas! the privilege of purchasing with our blood the happiness of those we love is a privilege granted only to a favoured few.

"I wish to be buried in the clothes I have on, Charlotte, for you have touched and consecrated them. I have made this request to your father.—My soul hovers over the grave!—I desire that my pockets may not be searched. The pink riban you wore on your bosom the first time I saw you surrounded by the children—sweet innocents, they still seem to dance round me!—O, kiss them a thousand times and tell them my melancholy story.— How instantly you became dear to me! How impossible it has been, since that moment, to tear myself from you!—This riban must be buried with me. You sent it to me on my birthday.— With what transports I received it!—Alas! alas! I did not think my journey would have ended thus! Be comforted, I beseech you, be comforted!

"They are loaded! It strikes twelve—I go—Charlotte! Charlotte, farewell! Farewell!"

One of the neighbours saw the flash and heard the report but, as all was still after it, he thought no more of it.

At about six in the morning his servant came in to bring him a candle. He found his master on the floor, and saw the pistol and the blood. He spoke to him and lifted him in his arms but received no reply—he still breathed. He ran for a surgeon and then to Albert's. Charlotte heard the bell and trembled in every limb. She awoke her husband and dressed herself. The servant came in and sobbed out the tidings—Charlotte fell senseless at Albert's feet. When the surgeon arrived, he was still on the floor. His pulse still beat—his extremities were cold. The ball had entered above the right eye and passed over the brain. The surgeon opened a vein in his arm—it bled and he continued to breathe.

From the blood on the chair, it was supposed he had done the deed sitting before his writing-table, and had fallen to the floor in his convulsions. He was found near the window, lying on his back, in a full dress, with boots, a grey frock, and yellow vest.

The house, the neighbourhood, the town were moved. Albert arrived. Werter was laid on the bed, and his head was bound up. His face had the sharpness of death. Not a muscle was convulsed. His respiration grew more difficult and unequal—his end was evidently approaching.

He had taken only a single glass of the wine. *Emilia Galotti* was lying open upon his table.

Of Albert's distress and Charlotte's grief I can say nothing.

The old Steward came the instant he received the intelligence —and kissed the dying man—and wept bitterly. His two elder sons followed him immediately and knelt by the bed and kissed his hands and cheeks in the agonies of grief—and the eldest,

who had always been his favourite, hung on his lips till the
spirit had fled and he was torn away by force. He died at noon.
The presence and arrangements of the Steward prevented all
disturbance. At about eleven at night, he was buried at the place
he had chosen. The Steward and his sons followed him to the
grave. Albert was not able. [Charlotte's life was in danger.]
He was borne by labourers. No priest attended.

[The third last sentence is unaccountably missing from Ticknor's translation. It is supplied here, with his permission, from
Victor Lange's version. Ed.]

The Quality of Ticknor's Translation

In examining Ticknor's translation I shall compare it briefly with the versions of Malthus, Render, and Pratt.[95] These were the only ones in circulation in America at the time, indeed until the latter half of the Nineteenth Century. It is with them that Ticknor's work would have competed for popular and critical favor. Inevitably, however, if a work such as this is to be read with more than antiquarian interest, it must have sound virtues which will stand with the best, of whatever date. Therefore I shall give a few parallel passages from the Boylan version[96] which Long in his article of 1915,[97] regarded as the best.

Let it be said immediately that Ticknor's translation is not perfect. There are inaccuracies and misinterpretations of which no modern scholar would be guilty. If these seem burdensome, remember the circumstances of the translating and the modest words "my first real exercises in German." By way of compensation, there are beauties of English in Ticknor's *Werter* which few modern translators, for all their verbal accuracy, can attain. It is this virtue that makes Ticknor's work readable, living, and exemplary.

The difficult constructions and the powerful content of the passage on Nature from I, May 10 [98] are well designed to make both these points clear. Neither is the passage, fine as it is, the best of Ticknor's English nor are its faults (with one exception) among his worst. It is a good representative selection. It reads:

> When the refreshing dampness of the valley descends around me—when the noon-day sun pours his unavailing beams on the impenetrable shades of my chosen wood, and only an occasional solitary ray pierces to its inmost recess—when I rest myself among the high grass by the waterfall—and thus brought nearer to the earth find there a thousand wonderful varieties of vegetation—when I feel myself grow familiar and intimate with the untold tribes of the insect world that inhabit the plants around me and with the unnumbered and innumerable forms of those that creep and those that fly, and thus feel the sensible presence of that Almighty being, who formed us in his own image, the very breath of that Eternal being, who supports and preserves us in perpetual delight—O, my dear friend, when this bright vision dawns on my senses, and the world and the heaven I have imagined descend and rest in my soul—then, in fervent aspiration, I often commune with myself and ask: Canst thou recall that impression? Canst thou breathe that spirit upon thy canvass, which lives and glows within thee; and make that canvass the mirror of thy soul, as thy soul is the mirror of the Everlasting God?—O my friend! I bow to the earth and sink under the power and majesty of the conception!*

---

*Wenn das liebe Tal um mich dampft und die hohe Sonne an der Oberfläche der undurchdringlichen Finsternis meines Waldes ruht und nur einzelne Strahlen sich in das innere Heiligtum stehlen, ich dann im hohen Grase am fallenden Bache liege und näher an der Erde tausend mannigfaltige Gräschen mir merkwürdig werden, wenn ich das Wimmeln der kleinen Welt zwischen Halmen, die unzähligen, unergründlichen Gestalten der Würmchen, der Mückchen näher an meinem Herzen fühle und fühle die Gegenwart des Allmächtigen, der uns nach seinem Bilde schuf, das Wehen

Perhaps the felicity of English and the sensitive and fluent expression of such a passage are not truly apparent until the passage is compared with others. The differences may at first glance seem exiguous. They are actually significant. This is the beginning of Boylan's:

> When the lovely valley teems with vapour around me, and the meridian sun strikes the upper surface of the impenetrable foliage of my trees, and but a few stray gleams steal into the inner sanctuary, then I throw myself down in the tall grass by the trickling stream, and as I lie close to the earth, a thousand unknown plants discover themselves to me.

Though he splits the long period, Boylan's language tends, by comparison to appear halting and uneven. He attempts more nearly verbatim accuracy than Ticknor, but the whole is not harmonious. "The lovely valley teems with vapour around me" is prosaic, "the meridian sun strikes the upper surface of the impenetrable foliage of my trees" is an arhythmic succession of dry words. Ticknor's phrasing is smooth. It can be read aloud without offense. "An occasional solitary ray pierces to its inmost recess" is more cohesive than the succession of "stray gleams," "steal," and "inner sanctuary." "I throw myself down in the tall grass by the trickling stream" is the best part of Boylan, a little more concrete and a little less high-flown than Ticknor's "I rest myself among the high grass by the waterfall." But "a thousand unknown plants discover themselves to me" is awkward. Ticknor's is not perfect but it is better.

If Boylan's style is to be judged less admirable than Ticknor's, what is there to say of Render's guidebook prose?

> When the lovely vale is covered with a mist, and the mid-day sun irradiates the skirts of my impenetrably gloomy wood, and but a few rays steal into the inmost sanctuary, I stretch myself along in the high grass by the side of the babbling brook, and while I lie close to the earth, a thousand varied tufts of grass, once too low for my notice, now attract my attention.

For the same passage Malthus wrote:

> Thin undulating vapours are spread over the plain; thick tufted trees defend me from the meridian sun, which only checkers my shade with a few rays. Here, extended on the long grass, near the fall of a brook, I admire the infinite variety of plants, and grow familiar with all the little insects that surround me, as they hum amongst the flowers or creep in the grass.

It is such passages as this that must have excited Ticknor's scorn for this "miserable imitation of a garbled French translation." The disadvantages of translating at second hand are uncomfortably plain. The English bears only the most general resemblance to Goethe's text. Whatever the

---

des Allliebenden, der uns in ewiger Wonne schwebend trägt und erhält, mein Freund, wenns dann um meine Augen dämmert und die Welt um mich her und der Himmel ganz in meiner Seele ruhn wie die Gestalt einer Geliebten, dann sehne ich mich oft und denke: Ach könntest du das wieder ausdrücken, könntest du dem Papiere das einhauchen, was so voll, so warm in dir lebt, dasz es würde der Spiegel deiner Seele, wie deine Seele ist der Spiegel des unendlichen Gotts!—Mein Freund—Aber ich gehe darüber zugrunde, ich erliege unter der Gewalt der Herrlichkeit dieser Erscheinungen.

quality of Malthus's language, and it is by no means always so uneven as the above, his work is largely invalidated by this inherent inaccuracy. Yet his version was the only medium of broad acquaintance with *Werther* until Boylan's translation in 1854. It can scarcely have given English and American readers an adequate idea of Goethe's text.

That Malthus could write fine English which, accurate to the letter or not, comes near to reproducing the spirit of Goethe, is plain from the rest of the same passage:

> Then I feel the divine breath of that all powerful Being which created us; whose eternal love supports and comforts us. A darkness spreads over my eyes; heaven and earth seem to dwell in my soul, and absorb all its powers, like the idea of a beloved mistress. Oh! that I could express, that I could describe, these great conceptions, with the same warmth, with the same energy that they are impressed on my soul! but the sublimity of them astonishes and overpowers me.

Pratt's version unfortunately speaks for itself, and quotation of the whole passage will suffice to characterize his pathetic translation.

> When the misty vapours sparkle in watery drops on the leafy boughs; and the deep shade of the thick foliage only emits a few faint streams of light and heat from the meridian fire, it is my delight to saunter beneath the arched shelter: then the fall grass forms my couch, and stretched out on the back of the rippling streamlet, I contemplate the great varieties of nature—myriads of insect beings who live in and exist upon them. How little did I once value those things—they now excite all my attention; they boldly declare to me that a celestial arm has placed us in existence, and that an immortal Omniscience upholds the world! At night, when darkness closes these beauties to my view, I paint on my imagination all that I have admired—all the wonderful works of nature; and my tongue bursts forth into the ejaculations of gratitude and piety! for the recollections they engender, like the portrait of an adored mistress, pregnant with the sweetest heart-springs of joy! My friend! I ardently wish that my powers of utterance could exhibit the extent of the feelings within. Alas! words are but insignificant representatives of such sublime conceptions, the magnitude of which confound and overwhelm the soul![99]

The comparisons offered are representative. As such, they indicate the indubitable superiority of Ticknor's translation over the versions then circulating in America and demonstrate his moderate but noticeable stylistic advantages over the more accurate Boylan text.

Close analysis of this same passage in Ticknor's translation will give a more precise notion of his technique and an occasional opportunity to see how the other translators fare in situations which caused Ticknor some difficulty.

The dominant characteristic of the passage is a freedom of phrase consonant with reasonable devotion to the original as Ticknor understood it. Though he omits only two words (*lieb* and *ausdrücken*) and makes up for one by an added "dear (friend)," he renders freely *sehne ich mich oft und denke* as "in fervent aspiration, I often commune with myself and ask" and *was so voll, so warm in dir lebt* as "which lives and glows within thee," as well as the difficult antecedent *das* by "that spirit." All of these are successful and pleasing, though the first (*sehne ich . . .*) may be over-expanded. The contemporary versions are hopeless. In Malthus, the first cannot be found; the construction of the second (*was so voll* . . .) is changed to read: "describe these great conceptions with the same warmth, with the same energy that they are impressed on my soul." In Pratt the first is "I ardently wish" and the second is lost in the verbiage. Render has inflated the first beyond Ticknor's extended phrase and away from the meaning: "Then do I frequently and fervently pour forth ejaculations." His version of the second is not bad: "what is so fully and warmly impressed on thy mind." Boylan's "then I often long and think" and "(all) that lives so full and warm within you" are literally correct. The first, however, is poor English. The second is an instance where a literal translation is almost completely successful. Whether it is better than Ticknor's is another question.

Often Ticknor expands a word or a phrase in the search for fluency of expression. *Gegenwart*, for example, is given as "sensible presence." More interesting: *um mich dampft* becomes, with dubious accuracy, "dampness . . . descends around me"; *der kleinen Welt zwischen Halmen* is "tribes of the insect world that inhabit the plants around me." All the other translators resort to some expansion of this sort. In these same instances, Render has: "covered with a mist"; "the various insects among the blades of grass." Pratt writes: "the misty vapours sparkle in watery drops on the leafy boughs" and "(varieties of nature) . . . and the myriads of insect beings who live in and exist upon them." Malthus has "thin undulating vapours are spread over the plain" (!) and "all the little insects that surround me." Boylan stays close to the original wording. But how much of a stylistic improvement are: "teems with vapour around me" and "little world among the stalks"?

Clearly, Ticknor does not attempt a verbatim rendering of the original. In allowing himself this degree of freedom he attains greater felicity of English, without at the same time doing violence to the essential spirit of Goethe's work.

There are, by contrast, illustrations of the danger of such freedom, or rather of its improper application. One expanded phrase seems unnecessary. "Pours his unavailing beams" is excessive for *ruht*. In another case Ticknor's expansion takes a significant direction. Here we have, on the one hand, a practice less laudable in translation and, on the other, a more significant indication of Ticknor's personal attitudes: *Himmel* is rendered "the heaven I have imagined." This is not an isolated case.

Directly related to the treatment of *Himmel* is the most noticeable fault in the section quoted, a fault which is at the same time one of the worst of the whole translation. Ticknor simply took umbrage at the simile *wie die Gestalt einer Geliebten* and cut it out. This is unpardonable, however interesting it may be as a sidelight on Ticknor. In several instances Ticknor's strict feeling of propriety in religious matters drove him to such literally Procrustean methods.   The other translators react interestingly to the boldness of Goethe's simile. Render has a very pleasant turn in "like the form of one I love." Aubry provided the key for Malthus. His version reads, with modest relish: "like the idea of a beloved mistress," and Boylan follows. Pratt is completely carried away: "like the portrait of an adored mistress, pregnant with the sweetest heart-springs of joy."

Another trait of Ticknor's work is exemplified by these translations: ...
merkwürdig werden by "find there"; *näher an meinem Herzen fühle* by
"I feel myself grow familiar and intimate with . . ."; *Würmchen, Mückchen*
by "those that creep and those thay fly." There is in all of these a
tendency to replace the specific by the general, the concrete by the abstract,
the immediate by the explained.

The original is changed to the point of license in "untold tribes" for
Wimmeln and to the point of error in "Canst thou" for *Könntest du* and
"I bow to the earth" for *ich gehe . . . zugrunde.* Whether the latter represent
out and out failure to understand the German is hard to say and actually
immaterial. They give a mistaken impression of the original.

The minor and major abuses of freedom in this one passage are a fair
index of Ticknor's shortcomings in general. The categories into which these
shortcomings fall are, though obviously overlapping, consistent and significant.

1) Generalization and explanation.
2) Toning down of what apparently seemed to Ticknor extravagance
and excess.
3) Alteration dictated by religious or moral scruple.
4) Errors, and brief omissions of indeterminate origin.

Tickor's penchant for generalizing or explaining is, of all his faults,
at once the most frequent and the least reprehensible. The two processes
run into one another and are easily considered together. Of their average
instance it may be said that examples worthy of note appear slightly less
than once a page in Ticknor's manuscript, that is to say less than twice a
page in the printed form. They are well distributed. Frequently they answer a clear need, as Ticknor seems to have felt it, to make more com-
prehensible a difficult or complex passage in Goethe's text. Frequently, on
the other hand, they seem unnecessary and, as may be gleaned from a
general reading of the *Werter* without reference to cases, their effect is
a certain loss of vividness and immediacy of feeling.

Typical of the fairly common preference for the explanatory generalization in place of the specific and individual figure are:

I May 17 *da tut mirs weh, wenn unser Weg nur eine kleine Strecke*
miteinander geht "I am really sorry we have little in common."

I July 24 *meine Empfindung an der Natur, bis aufs Steinchen, aufs*
Gräschen herunter "my perception of natural beauty, even in its minutest
details."

In one passage, II Dec. 24, he reverses his usual practice by translating
Kein Und, kein Bindewörtchen "Not an 'if' or an 'end'."

Transition to pure explanation appears in I May 13 *ich brauche Wiegen-*
gesang "I need only a little poetry to soothe me." This procedure results in
the utter ruin of a pungent metaphor in II March 24 (*Den schönen Lauf, den*
ihr Sohn gerade zum Geheimenrat und Gesandten ansetzte, so auf einmal
Halte zu sehen) und rückwärts mit dem Tierchen in den Stall "returned to
his original insignificance."

Explanation replacing, to a degree, translation often means the rendering of Goethe's idea as Ticknor understood it, without the acceptance of

Goethe's wording. The practice is not laudable and the result not overly accurate. The only factor to be adduced in defense of Ticknor is the immensely greater sinning of the other early translators.

Note how almost every idea in the following passage is reproduced, but rephrased or explained in Ticknor's rendition. II Nov. 26 *einen Mann, den ich jeden Tag mehr verehren musz, einen weiten groszen Kopf und der deswegen nicht kalt ist, weil er viel übersieht; aus dessen Umgange so viel Empfindung für Freundschaft und Liebe hervorleuchtet* "a man whom I honour more and more every day, a man of uncommon talents and of a wide circumspection and yet of an affectionate temper—a man who you instantly see is formed for friendship."

Explaining, as might be expected, often means toning down, for example: I July 1 . . . *dasz ich drüber zugrunde gehen würde*" (told me) it would impair my health."

In general, Ticknor, if he changes the original at all, quiets extravagant or violent utterances. Examples: I May 30 *Ich hab in meinem Leben die dringende Begierde und das heisze sehnliche Verlangen nicht in dieser Reinheit gesehen, ja wohl kann ich sagen, in dieser Reinheit nicht gedacht und geträumt* "Never did I meet or imagine an attachment at once so passionate and so pure." II March 16 *dasz ich ihm den Degen durch den Leib stoszen könnte* "that I might take vengeance on his life." II Sept. 12 *Sein Kusz . . . ist nicht ganz ohne Begierde* "His favours . . . are not entirely disinterested." Anyone who wishes may find many more.

Let it be said that the sum of all instances like the above is far outweighed by the fact that Ticknor, whatever his doubts about its propriety, renders fully and accurately most of the impetuous emotion of Werther. There are even a few passages where the feeling is intensified. Needless to say they are rare (and they may represent an increase of spiritual or religious fervor rather than of individual passion). 1 July 13 is typical: *Gefühl des wahren Verhältnisses* "sober certainty of waking bliss." One burst of stronger language from Ticknor comes as a distinct surprise: II Feb. 8 *kein schöner Tag . . . , den mir nicht jemand verdorben oder verleidet hätte* "not . . . a single fine day . . . which some untoward blockhead has not spoiled for me."

An interesting minor corollary to Ticknor's softening of Goethe's language is his not infrequent abandonment of two grammatical devices of vivification, the historical present and the superlative. Instances of the former appear, for example, in I Aug. 12, II March 15, March 16, Nov. 30, and in the scene after the suicide; of the latter in II Dec. 24 *elendesten, erbärmlichsten*, and II Feb. 20 *feierlichst*.

Related, again, to the preceding category is the group of infrequent but inescapable instances of religious and moral censorship. The most interesting single aspect of Ticknor's religious editing proceeds from his attitude toward the words *Himmel* and *himmlisch*. These are, in Puritan strictness, translated literally only when they are theologically literal. Otherwise they are the victims of circumlocution or omission. For example: I July 16 *der himmlische Atem thres Mundes* becomes "her breath." I Aug. 30 *an dem himmlischen Ausdruck ihrer Worte* "to the enchantment of her conversation." The identical compulsion turns *Paradies* in I Aug. 18 into "an imaginary paradise" and banishes *Teufel!* in II March 15. In II Sept. 12, to be sure, a presumably non-theological *himmlisch* is translated "heavenly."

As offensive to Ticknor's sensibilities as the simile in I May 10 was the shocking proposal of Werther in his first letter after the climax scene, where he wrote: *ich fliege dir entgegen und fasse dich und bleibe bei dir vor dem Angesichte des Unendlichen in ewigen Umarmungen.* He changes it to "I shall fly to meet you—then I shall claim you, and before the face of the everlasting God we shall meet and dwell forever."

Seen in this cold light, Ticknor's moral and religious censorship seems a little petty, a little prudish, and unfair to the reader. He occasionally treats passion with excessive circumspection. He is more cautious about religion than many a seminarian. It remains a fact, however, that his age did not share our strict standards of the translator's duty and also that it insisted on drawing a line of acceptability in religious matters. We of a different age may choose to regard Ticknor's qualms with the respectful good humor of a presumably more enlightened spirit.

The sum of Ticknor's various changes affects the tenor of Goethe's novel, and the direction of that effect is largely consistent. A portion of Werther's expressed and implicit rebellion against the conventions of his century is obscured or lost by the very process of generalizing and toning down his language. There is less of the Storm and Stress, with its vigorous, if frustrated, individualism, and slightly more of the polite and temperate Enlightenment. This is a proportion with which the young Goethe would have had little sympathy. *Werter* is, by moderate measure, more restrained, more dignified, more respectable, more fastidious, and more pious than *Werther*. It must be remembered that these are changes of tolerable degree, not absolute reversals of mood, but their impact can be felt in a careful reading of the book. More important perhaps, with the loss of part, small though it be, of the violence of Werther's temperament goes the loss of a corresponding part of the motivation and credibility of his violent end.

A striking generic resemblance, not to say precedent, for Ticknor's altering is to be found in Goethe himself and in this very work. The changes from the *Werther* of 1774 to that of 1787 come unbidden to mind. Consider II Sept. 15:

> 1774: Man möchte sich dem Teufel ergeben, Wilhelm, über all die Hunde, die Gott auf Erden duldet, ohne Sinn und Gefühl an dem wenigen, was drauf noch was wert ist.
> 1787: Man möchte rasend werden, Wilhelm, dasz es Menschen geben soll ohne Sinn und Gefühl an dem Wenigen, was auf Erden noch einen Wert hat.

Or Lotte's night of torment after the disastrous reading of Ossian:

> 1774: Die liebe Frau hatte die letzte Nacht wenig geschlafen; ihr Blut war in einer fieberhaften Empörung, und tausenderlei Empfindungen zerrütteten ihr Herz. Wider ihren Willen fühlte sie tief in ihrer Brust das Feuer von Werthers Umarmungen und zugleich stellten sich ihr die Tage ihrer unbefangenen Unschuld, des sorglosen Zutrauens auf sich selbst in doppelter Schöne dar . . . .
> 1787: Die liebe Frau hatte die letzte Nacht wenig geschlafen;

was sie gefürchtet hatte, war entschieden, auf eine Weise entschieden, die sie weder ahnen noch fürchten konnte; ihr sonst so
rein und leicht flieszendes Blut war in einer fieberhaften Empö-
rung, tausenderlei Empfindungen zerrütteten das schöne Herz.
War es das Feuer von Werthers Umarmungen, das sie in ihrem
Busen fühlte? War es Unwille über seine Verwegenheit? War es
eine unmutige Vergleichung ihres gegenwärtigen Zustandes mit
jenen Tagen ganz unbefangener, freier Unschuld und sorglosen
Zutrauens an sich selbst? . . . .

Ticknor went farther in his alteration of the text. Furthermore, the
novel was Goethe's, not his. But the generalizing and tempering is definitely
similar.

The other face of the coin is, in its own way, equally significant. The
realization of how much emotion and passion and violence Ticknor loyal-
ly left in his translation poses again, this time with literary evidence, the
fascinating question which belongs most properly to a biography of this
distinguished man: To what degree were Ticknor's scholarly urbanity and
assured Puritanism countered in his youth by an unsuspected current of that
sensitivity, frustration, and explosive melancholy of which Werther is the
extreme symbol? It is scarcely necessary to repeat that this same basic
loyalty to Goethe's text also answers a question: By which of the early
translations might *Werther* best have been known to the English-speaking
world?

The final problem of omissions and errors is largely a statistical one.
The two major gaps have been noted. Others are very brief, often assign-
able to one of Ticknor's established tendencies, rarely the result of what
could conceivably be termed prudent avoidance. In only two cases (II Sept. 6,
and final paragraph) have I included in the text, in brackets, a word or
sentence omitted by Ticknor. The inclusion of these elements rests on the
twin facts that they are essential to the story and that their omission may
well have been an oversight. There is a final and not inconseqential residue
of omissions, usually of a single word, the explanation for which may
simply be the lesser vigilance of the early translator. In my analysis of the
text I noted 36 omissions (of more than a word or two). The deletion of
both footnotes to I June 16 and of the one footnote to II Feb. 17 might
be especially noted.

There is no need to make a catalogue of errors. One cannot say of the
Sorrows of Werter as Faust did of Adams' *Oberon*: "Only very rarely can
we pick a flaw." A complete list, including minutiae, would be long. The
most important lapses are interesting in what they reveal of Ticknor's
inadequacies but also in what they mark as translation hazards implicit in
the time and the circumstances.

Here, presented with what should be an unnecessary recommendation of
clemency, are examples of the worst of Ticknor's errors.

Footnote to I July 1 *Wir haben nun von Lavatern eine treffliche Predigt
hierüber unter denen über das Buch Jonas* "There is, however, an exquisite sermon against it by Lavater—to say nothing of the Book of Jonah."

The entire second half of I July 11, starting about with *Als unsere
Haushaltung stärker wurde*, is very bad. Ticknor failed to understand that
the hard-pressed housewife had lifted from the cashbox the extra money
denied her by her parsimonious husband. In consequence he mistranslated not

only this but the entire remainder of the letter. It is to be noted that this passage, especially the last paragraph, caused considerable havoc among the early translators.

At the end of II Dec. 24 Ticknor misinterpreted the relation of Miss B's aunt and her officer husband and failed understandably to see the meaning of *das eherne Jahrhundert* and *das eiserne.*

Ticknor's version of II Nov. 30 is easily the worst in *Werter,* a compend of errors and shortcomings, misreadings and omissions. It even contains a genuine howler. Worst of all, much of the felicity of expression is gone. The unhappy evidence is available to anyone with a German *Werther.* In this one passage Ticknor confirms the true superiority of his translation over those of his predecessors and contemporaries by, for once, collapsing to their level, for it is true that Render could have written as well.

Two special considerations attach themselves automatically to any discussion of errors in Ticknor's work. They are, indeed, far more important than the detailed analysis itself. First, such close scrutiny of Malthus, Render, or Pratt would be, by the nature of their texts, utterly impossible. Ticknor's is the first version to which strict standards can be applied. Secondly, we must recall the circumstances of the translation. The entire country offered no formal training in the language which would remotely prepare for a task so extensive and so demanding. Indeed it scarcely boasted any instruction at all. Ticknor was largely self-taught. He worked in New England, thousands of miles from the home of the language he studied and from the scene of his chosen book. He worked without model and without precedent. Yet he produced a distinguished translation, "worthy of the inimitable original."

NOTES TO INTRODUCTION AND APPENDIX

[1] *NAR*, IV, 258.

[2] *Life, Letters, and Journals of George Ticknor* (Boston, 1876), I, p. 12. Cited hereafter as *LLJ*. There is an edition of 1909, with an introduction by Ferris Greenslet.

[3] Orie W. Long, "Werther in America," *Studies in Honor of John Albrecht Walz* (Lancaster, Pa., 1941), p. 111, n. 85.

[4] Typescript of Ticknor's journals (in Dartmouth Library), IV, p. 417, footnote. Cited hereafter as TJ. Journal references will be made to the typescript, though the manuscript has in all cases been checked for correct reading. If all or part of a quotation has previously been published, the source will be indicated.

[5] I thank Miss Hazel Joslyn, librarian of the Alumni Archives in Baker Library, for her kindness in helping me locate this manuscript and other Ticknor manuscript materials. I first reported on the MS in "George Ticknor's *Sorrows of Young Werter*," *Comparative Literature*, I, No. 4 (1949), pp. 360-372.

[6] Orie W. Long, *Literary Pioneers* (Cambridge, 1935), pp. 3-62. Van Wyck Brooks, *Flowering of New England* (New York, 1936). J. D. M. Ford, "George Ticknor," *Dictionary of American Biography*, XVIII (1936), pp. 525-528. Henry Grattan Doyle, "George Ticknor," *Modern Language Journal*, XXII, No. 1 (October, 1937), 3-18.

[7] Doyle, p. 7.

[8] A.B. Faust, *Oberon . . . Translated by John Quincy Adams* (New York, 1940), pp. xiv-xv.

[9] TJ, IV, p. 417, footnote. In another note to the same passage he says (in original MS only, dated 1850): "I translated the whole of Werther as an exercise in learning German before I left home."

[10] *LLJ*, pp. 11-12.

[11] George Ticknor, *Life of Prescott* (Boston, 1864), p. 9.

[12] See H. S. Jantz, "German Thought and Literature in New England, 1620-1820," *Journal of English and Germanic Philology*, XLI (1942), pp. 1-45. Quotations in this paragraph are from Jantz, pp. 2-3 and p. 2, note 4.

[13] Ticknor's memory was always one of his strong points and the source of much praise. Charles Norton, for example, wrote to James Russell Lowell in 1860, praising Ticknor for "so strong a memory." See Long, *Literary Pioneers*, p. 236, n. 165. In its obituary the Boston *Post* of January 26, 1871, referred to "exact habits," "wonderful precision of . . . mind," "laborious revision that few other men could have accomplished" and concludes its article: "Until very recently his mind has retained its pristine vigor, barring, perhaps, a certain loss of memory, a faculty in which he has always been signally powerful." These remarks are from an article totally free from the usual dithyrambics and one which has, for instance, no delusions about popularity or liberalism in Ticknor and no excessive claims for his fame. The Boston *Journal*, of the same date, specifies the brevity of the decline in Ticknor's faculties: "It is only within a few months that his remarkable memory has shown evidence of decay."

[14] Cf. Jantz, p. 2, n. 4 and p. 42.

[15] *Journal of the Proceedings of the Anthology Society*, ed. M. A. De-Wolfe Howe (Boston, 1910), p. 285 and p. 278.

[16] P. 270.

[17] Ticknor's *Review of the Memoirs of the Rev. Joseph Buckminster and the Rev. Joseph Stevens Buckminster* (Cambridge, 1849). The main interest is on personal and theological lines only.

¹⁸ There is no dearth of references to the Vaughans in Ticknor's journals. On only one occasion is there any exchange of German literary interests. In London on June 16, 1815, he "dined at the benevolent Mr. Vaughan's with Dr. Schwabe, a learned German clergyman, who gave us considerable information about the state of letters in Germany." (TJ, I, p. 61.)

¹⁹ See Jantz, pp. 35-42.

²⁰ P. 36.

²¹ For the letters in question, see American Antiquarian Society, BII, 52. James Freeman's letter to Bentley (March 24, 1815) introduces Ticknor and his projected trip to Europe "chiefly for the sake of improving himself in literature," and requests "letters of introduction to your friends on the other side of the Atlantick . . . to add . . . to the recommendations which he has obtained from President Adams, President Jefferson, and other persons whom you esteem." Ticknor's accompanying letter is a purely formal note assuring Buckminster "that my objects are exclusively literary and scientifick—and that I shall visit England, France, Italy and Greece and pass a year of study at some one of the German Universities."

²² On Bancroft's interests in German, see M. A. DeWolfe Howe, Life and Letters of George Bancroft (New York, 1908), I, p. 29, etc.

²³ Long, Literary Pioneers, p. 63.

²⁴ P. 64.

²⁵ P. 66.

²⁶ See Jantz, p. 26, p. 37, etc.

²⁷ J. Hatfield, New Light on Longfellow (Boston, 1933), p. 13.

²⁸ See Jantz, p. 31, on Vaughan's translation of Hirtzel.

²⁹ Long, Literary Pioneers, p. 233, n. 117.

³⁰ "Edward Everett's College Life," Old and New, IV, p. 19.

³¹ A. Peabody, Harvard Reminiscences (Boston, 1888), p. 117. Unaccountably, Jantz includes this passage among the misleading references.

³² Orie W. Long, Thomas Jefferson and George Ticknor (Williamstown, Mass., 1933), p. 13.

³³ There is a further parallel in Ticknor's statement on our "absolute ignorance" of German education, in his Remarks on the Character of . . . Edward Everett (Boston, 1865), p. 11.

³⁴ On all these matters the main source is Jantz, passim.

³⁵ Old and New, IV, pp. 18-27.

³⁶ Howe (Bancroft, I, p. 29) checked Bancroft's library cards at Harvard during 1816-18 and found "toward the end a preponderance of works of German scholarship and letters."

³⁷ Ida G. Everson, George Henry Calvert (New York, 1944), p. 71.

³⁸ The external history of the review is of itself unimportant, but it emphasizes the close personal contacts that give so much of Boston intellectual life the stamp of corporate unity. At the supper of woodcocks and the ensuing program John Kirkland (soon President of Harvard) presided; Jacob Bigelow, James Savage, Kirkland, and Ticknor reported to the Club. There is no record of others in attendance, except that Buckminster was assigned a future review. Andrews Norton, and Samuel Thacher, who was the intermediary of Ticknor's information on the Göttingen library, were actively concerned in the business of the meeting, though not present. Ticknor, only three years out of Dartmouth, had had the task assigned him at the July 31 meeting where W. S. Shaw entertained, and it was Shaw who later got him Adams' copy of Werther.

³⁹ Identified as Ticknor's by Savage's write-in on his copy. See Howe, Anthology Society, p. 317 and p. 327.

⁴⁰ IX (1810), pp. 191-194.

⁴¹ LLJ, I, p. 120.

⁴² De l'Allemagne (Paris, 1814), II, p. 293.

⁴³ Sec. 6 under "Goethe" in an untitled MS volume in the Alumni Archives at Dartmouth.

[44] XXXII (1786), p. 144.

[45] The article he refers to, entitled "Auszug aus einem Briefe aus London vom 7ten März," makes it plain that the English have ill-used the German language in their translations, and what is worse, have by no means reciprocated for the large number of German translations of English works. "Das einzige Buch," complains the author, "das ziemlich allgemein geworden, ist Werther, and diesz ist doch nur aus dem Französischen übersetzt." It is no surprise that Ticknor should still refer to "our English," as if it were the only one, in spite of the seven English versions that had by this time appeared. Boylan, writing in 1854, still thought *Werther* had never been translated from German into English, though he too knew the Malthus retranslation.

[46] *Goethes Briefwechsel mit Georg und Caroline Sartorius*, ed. Else von Monroy (Weimar, 1931), p. 162.

[47] Long, *Literary Pioneers*, p. 7.

[48] S. H. Goodnight, *German Literature in American Magazines prior to 1846*, University of Wisconsin Philology and Literature Series, IV (1907), p. 65.

[49] *American Review*, III, No. 5 (1812), p. 53.

[50] *The Testament of Werther in Poetry and Drama* (Cambridge, Mass. 1949), p. 193.

[51] In 1800 Bentley, speaking perhaps from his own wider acquaintance, wrote differently: "As to the works of Wieland and Goethe, they have been long in the hands of the public . . ." (Jantz, p. 41). Like so much connected with Bentley, this is rather exceptional than characteristic.

[52] Best for this country in Orie W. Long's "Werther in America" (see note 3).

[53] Long, "Werther in America," p. 88.

[54] Orie W. Long, "English Translations of Goethe's Werther," *Journal of English and Germanic Philology*, XIV (1915), 173.

[55] P. 191.

[56] From "The passion of Werther" to "calm and tranquil" he copies a page and a half with only a few alterations. In his "Advertisement of the Translator" Render calls Aubry's French version "multilated" and says of Malthus: "In an edition which had thus been prepared through the medium of a second language, the spirit of the original not only was in a great measure evaporated but many interesting passages, and several entire letters were omitted"!

[57] *LLJ*, I, p. 9.

[58] Henry Adams, *A Catalogue of the Books of John Quincy Adams Deposited in the Boston Athenaeum* (Boston, 1938), pp. 30-31.

[59] TJ, I, p. 104. Also at length in Long, *Literary Pioneers*, p. 10.

[60] TJ, I, p. 122.

[61] *Life of Joseph Cogswell*, pp. 55-56.

[62] TJ, III, p. 340. Quoted in Long, *Literary Pioneers*, p. 28.

[63] TJ, IV, pp. 416-418. Quoted in part in Long, *op. cit.*, p. 30.

[64] *LLJ*, II, p. 58. See also p. 59, p. 64, p. 65.

[65] TJ, VI, pp. 934-935. Quoted in part in *LLJ*, II, p. 72.

[66] TJ, VI, p. 936. Quoted in Long, *Literary Pioneers*, p. 60; in part in *LLJ*, II, p. 73.

[67] TJ, IV, p. 417, footnote.

[68] TJ, I, pp. 135-136.

[69] *LLJ*, I, p. 13, 260.

[70] The omitted reference is presumably to Part II, Chapter 28, although Mme. de Staël's words referred to Goethe himself. Other references by Ticknor in these sections of his notes are sufficiently full and correct unless otherwise annotated.

[71] *Authentische Briefe des Hauptmanns von Arenswald* . . . The full name is Gottlieb Georg Ernst von Arenswald. The editor was Karl Gottfried Küttner.

72 The two Weygand editions.
73 The Himburg edition.
74 *Dictionnaire des ouvrages anonymes et pseudonymes* (Paris, 1806).
75 At Erlangen.
76 Goedeke's *Grundrisz* spells Deyverdun. "Paris" appears to be wrong.
77 Comte Henri de la Bedoyère.
78 *Lettres de Werther à Charlotte* in *Mélanges* . . . etc.
79 The first Malthus edition.
80 *The Sorrows of Werter: a Poem.*
81 Gaetano Grassi.
82 Westée's translation.
83 1788.
84 Ticknor's library at Dartmouth still contains his copy of this rare item.
85 Title slightly different in Goedeke.
86 "Riebe" is the correct spelling.
87 One of Ticknor's few important bibliographical errors. The name is Göchhausen.
88 October 3.
89 H. G. von Bretschneider, *Eine entsetzliche Mordgeschichte von dem jungen Werther.*
90 . . . *Werthers.* Translated from Sinner's *Les malheurs de l'amour* (Berne, 1775).
91 Apparently should be 1778.
92 Garve's letter. See J. J. Engel, *Schriften* (Berlin, 1844), I, pp. 14-20.
93 *Neue Bibliothek der schönen Wissenschaften und der freyen Künste.*
94 Orie W. Long in "Werther in America," p. 91.
95 The editions used: Malthus—*The Sorrows and Sympathetic Attachments of Werter, by Mr. Goethe, Doctor of the Civil Law* (Philadelphia, 1784); and *The Sorrows of Werter* . . . (Chiswick, 1822). Render—*The Sorrows of Werter, Translated from the German of Baron Goethe, by William Render, D. D.* (Concord, N. H., 1824). Pratt—*The Sorrows of Werter, from the German of Baron Goëthe, a New Translation Revised and Compared with all the Former Editions—The Second Edition—by Dr. Samuel Pratt* (London, 1809). The Goethe text is cited from the Welt-Goethe-Ausgabe, *Goethes Werke*, ed. A. Kippenberg et al. (Mainz, 1932), vol. 16.
96 *Novels and Tales by Göethe* . . . *Translated Chiefly by R. D. Boylan, Esq.* (London, 1854). Boylan's version was revised and reworked by Victor Lange for his edition, *The Sorrows of Young Werther* . . . (New York, 1949), the best English translation available to the modern reader.
97 *Journal of English and Germanic Philology*, XIV, p. 201.
98 Citations from all texts of *Werther* will be made by (Part) I or II, followed by date of letter, or by similar headings.
99 An amusing supplement to this turgid passage is Pratt's version of Ossian, in which, at a critical point, we read:
Say, why dost thou wake me! O gale!
It answers, "With dew-drops I'm wet—
But the time of my fading draws nigh,
The blast when my leaves shall all set."